How to

Wake

Early

The Book About How to Wake Up
Early

*(Proven Methods to Rising Early & Accomplishing
Your Goals)*

Richard Sosa

Published By **Jessy Lindsay**

Richard Sosa

How to Wake Early: The Book About How to Wake Up Early (Proven Methods to Rising Early & Accomplishing Your Goals)

ISBN 978-1-7774561-4-6

Legal & Disclaimer

Table Of Contents

Chapter 1: Why Is A Morning Routine So Important?... 1

Chapter 2: What Do Successful People Do Every Morning?... 7

Chapter 3: Power Off Your Evening Routine 15

Chapter 4: Power On Your Morning Routine 22

Chapter 5: Your New Morning Routine System 33

Chapter 6: Your New Morning System The Mind 54

Chapter 7: Your Completed Morning Routine 105

Chapter 8: Collect Habits 111

Chapter 9: Meditation.......................... 121

Chapter 10: Breakfast 133

Chapter 11: Get It Done 147

Chapter 12: The 30day Morning Routine
Challenge 167

Chapter 13: The Benefits Of Waking Up At
5 A.M 171

Chapter 14: The Pros And Cons Of Rising
Early 181

Chapter 1: Why Is A Morning Routine So Important?

"Lose one hour early in the morning, and you'll be searching for it all day long. it."

Richard Whately

The significance of our morning mood (and consequently the routine which creates the mood) can cause ripple effects throughout the day. Every hour, waves after waves of ripples continue to roll out. The process begins when we drop the very initial drop. This is, what we think about at the beginning of our day.

It is clear that the thoughts we think about in the morning provide the foundation to our brain's processes all day long. Research suggests that an upbeat mood boosts the level of happiness and efficiency throughout the day. However, the reverse is also true. An unhappiness in the beginning of the day will lead to being frustrated and inefficient working day. No matter whether you're heading on a job for the day or school, or simply enjoying your day off being in a good outlook in the early morning will enable you to attain the most sought-after and important quality of all: real happiness. This is about having fun and enjoying life to the fullest as well as being more efficient and friendly are some of the positive outcomes.

Why do we have do we need a routine? Do you not find happiness more easily achieved doing things spontaneously? Sure, having a routine will put you on the path to boredom. The same thing, every day is repetitive, surely? But it's not.

A routine simply means providing you with an outline to get you started on your day.

Instead of feeling disorganized which can cost you time and energy as a result the routine streamlines your life and winds with more flexibility. One might think that to have a routine to bind you instead, however it provides you with more room to be reflective and focus on whatever you want to accomplish in a relaxed and stress-free manner. Also, you'll have an abundance of time since you perform your tasks in a punctual and organized manner. An unorganized lifestyle is not will help you become the person you'd like to become.

However, even if you're an extremely impulsive individual, the structure of your routine will give you a start where you can take a different direction. It is possible to plan to run in the morning however, you realize that you're unmotivated to run, and decide to skip it instead of spending an hour in the studio. You don't have to approach your routine as a boot camp nevertheless, it's essential to establish some sort of routine to keep you motivated.

Fitness, diet as well as sleeping routines are huge factors that affect your overall energy. They also play a major role to boost your mood. Experts believe that sleep as well as nutrition as well as exercise are all factors that contribute to depression, as are methods of relieving depression.

A healthy diet that includes all three begins at the beginning of each day. An evening of rest will give the drive to perform an exercise session that will give you the energy to eat the healthy meal. All of us should aim to achieve the best night's rest. If you're suffering from trouble sleeping, do not spend your time sleeping through the night and grumpy days. This is one of the conditions that are essential to take care of. Consult a doctor or an herbalist to rid the problem and help you get to a better place.

Your routine can help you determine the things that are essential for you. Personal health and nutrition which are essential to living. All of us will wash up and have breakfast in the early morning. However, how you do it and the activities you include in your routine will allow you to evaluate what it is that you value.

If you're a writer, then you should take 20 minutes off for writing. Do you hold any public positions? It is possible to put a special focus on the appearance of your persona by making an agenda that will keep you in good shape as well as allowing extra time to take care of your private grooming. Moms who stay at home could choose to spend time alone time during her routine, as she is spending a lot of time helping the needs of others. A musician who is aspiring might decide to practice best when he gets up at 5 am. the next morning he'll get himself up and performing.

Your personality is distinctive. Try not to come up with an routine according to what you imagine you think a routine ought to be. Instead, consider what is important to you and try it out to find your own personal preferences. Be aware that the aim isn't to become an authority figure or perform something you're not willing to do. Your routine is designed to aid you.

Chapter 2: What Do Successful People Do Every Morning?

"Every day, you are faced with two options: either sleep in a dream or get up and pursue your goals. Your choice is up to you!" -unknown

Prior to establishing your personal routine It is advantageous to glance at the lives of influential individuals and find out what they do to ensure a positive mindset and a pleasant morning routine. A lot of successful individuals have adopted the routine which accommodates their busy life. Remember that your routine might not focus on the demands of a full-time job. Your morning routines of people who have made it big and those still on the climb may differ. Follow these advices from professionals to ensure your achievement in your everyday life. Consider using them to enable you to conquer larger areas in your career and personal life, too.

Barack Obama faced many decisions in his 44th presidency of the United States. To reduce the amount of choices that he had to take throughout his life, he developed his own routine when he was president that let him conserve time as well as energy. Obama puts a lot of emphasis on his family members, in spite of the ever-changing chores he has to complete in his capacity as Nobel Prize winner and former president. Obama realized that even the smallest tasks take time away from the things that matter most to him the family and his wife. This is why there is a plan of the drinks he'll consume each early morning (green tea, or juice from oranges) as well as what clothing will he wear. As he did not have any worries about the clothes he would wear, he was able to save time. By reducing time in spite of demands from the president, he was in a position to help the people he cherishes.

People who have experienced their success, as well as the hectic routine that often comes with it, decide to organize their outfits ahead of time. Mark Zuckerberg, CEO of Facebook is also known to wear the same clothes each day. It assists him in focusing on the goals he has set for himself as he is confident that he will look good wearing the same tried-and-true outfit that is now his go-to outfit.

Tips: It's possible to alter your style each day make sure you have a couple of "go-to" clothes which are neat and well-stocked to be tucked away in your closet for those times when you're not able to have time to do so.

Spiritual leader and activist Mohandas Gandhi led India to the independence of India. Also, he was an example for the rest of the world to live in a peaceful, healthy lifestyle and being a huge political regent. He was up by 4:00 morning each day. He then began to pray, and led others in prayer, before writing down the now-famous thoughts and quotes. At 7:00, it wasn't until that he began thinking about breakfast, and the next day. This means that for three minutes each day, Gandhi was able to concentrate on his spiritual peace as well as inner principles. When he awoke early, he was able to avoid all the noise of the external world and was able to gain insight into his own inner world. Particularly, in this Hindu practice, religious guides and seekers are encouraged to rise early to avoid this issue. From 4:00 until 5:15 is also known as Brahma Muhurtha. It is the ideal time to meditate.

TIP: Make an effort to get up earlier than you think is possible however, you can ease into this routine by getting up 5 minutes earlier each morning. After two months, you'll be in a position to wake up at a time earlier than.

Very few people are able to boast having won the Olympic gold medal. It requires a lot of practice, determination and a ferocious spirit. For Michael Phelps, the record in gold medals for all Olympian the world, winning is an act of calculation. Phelps was a professional athlete who worked all year round in the prime of his athletic career He has learned to plan his actions, which has made him more than just a winner and the top athlete of the best in the world. The routines he follows every day reveal a pattern that helps to refine him. He wakes up at the exact time every day. He rises around 6:30 am after showering, he is dressed, and sets off for breakfast around 7:00 at the exact time. He enjoys a large meal (sometimes more than 1200 to 1000 calories when working out, 6 times higher than the average individual!). The stretching begins at 8:15 doing the same stretch every throughout the day, in the same pattern. He then begins to do laps around the pool, and after 9:00, he takes time to relax and listen to songs which is the same tune that he plays every throughout the day.

Phelps' routine reveals a remarkable discovery. When he repeats the same activities daily, he's growing the myelin layer of the neurons in his body. The neurologists have found that regular practice can thicken a layer of white matter on the cells of brain that is known as myelin. Myelin gets thicker it allows neurons to function faster and are more efficient. So, the greater myelin there is, the greater skill. Repeating the same actions every day helps strengthen specific neural pathways required to perform well at a particular job. Think of a crossword puzzle. If you repeat the daily over the course of a week, you'll have the ability to finish it in a matter of the time of minutes or in minutes or. A different puzzle demands different neural pathways every day starts right from scratch. Repeating the exact routine every day has enabled Michael Phelps to perfect himself starting from the inside. Every time he repeats the laps and stretches the brain's neurons are working faster and quicker. The brain is now stronger than his body, guiding him to the success he has achieved.

TIP: Much like Phelps You can gain from repeating the same routines each day. It doesn't matter if you're perfecting a particular track on the guitar by performing every morning, or finally mastering the yoga posture, constant repetition strengthens your body as well as your brain.

The majority of those who have succeeded in reaching success are like you. Keep in mind that success is about achieving your goals. It is possible that you possess the same potential as some of the top performers athletes in the world, however If you don't discover it, you'll never achieve anything. Making a point to be intentional in your daily activities will provide you with the ability to access your potential. You shouldn't be a model for any other person, regardless of the ideal or successful person may seem. Consider the root of their accomplishment, and realize that it was not a result of chance or luck alone However, conscious decisions will result in the results you want to achieve.

Chapter 3: Power Off Your Evening Routine

It's been discussed before that an ideal morning begins by getting a great night's sleep. What do you do in the direction of getting that ideal sleep that leaves you refreshed and rejuvenated? This might seem away for those who tend to wake awake tired and exhausted. However, there's a myriad of options to ensure you're getting enough sleep and get ready for the next day.

It's a race to go, go, and move around all day. Your motor is energized and you're in motion. And when you go to bale, your wheels continue to spin and are working. The practice of a regular nighttime routine can help you take a break. The thoughts and anxieties you have will go away. The anxiety will go away. Then you'll be able to lay to sleep just like you're sitting in a cloud. You'll feel light and sassy.

One of the major changes for professionals who go during the transition from work to leisure time is changing clothes.

The simple act of putting your physically out of your office and in a relaxed state. If you're transitioning between night and day that same concept can be very beneficial. Beware of falling into a slumber in your clothes that you're in. Get yourself some comfortable and comfy sleepwear of your choice. It's a thrilling sensation to remove your clothing that is covered in dust and dirt from the day. Imagine your mind letting go of all worries and worries while at the at the same time. You'll feel fresh and relaxed when you put on your soft pajamas.

Prior to changing into your evening wear clean your face using an odor-free soap that has calming characteristics, like lavender. The pleasant feeling of smooth clothes and sweet smells will put you into the state of relaxation.

If you are dealing with a lot of stress you might be tempted to seek to get away from the stress by watching television and films to keep the mind off things. It can work on the surface, however be aware of what you watch on your screen. Many of the most appealing programmes make us feel wired and anxious following their viewing such as graphic news stories.

Try to stay away from using electronic device for at least 30 minutes prior to bedtime.

It's a lot more beneficial to relax with an enjoyable book in the evening rather than watching a TV program. A good quality TV like documentaries about nature or educational shows is a great alternative to wind down, but be aware that any artificial light can be stimulant no matter what it is.

When you are at the time where you are trying to relax and relax, the bright light on screens sends a false message. Humans are complicated machines. We're not responsible for what we are doing. The mechanisms that are running within our brains and bodies can overwhelm us. But once we know these processes, we can utilize these to benefit ourselves. By doing this, selecting the appropriate stimulus (calming and relaxing activities) will tell our brain to relax.

Then what? If you fall asleep You'll feel the results. While you're lying down, you should take five minutes to think about your entire day. Which areas you did well and what you did wrong. Be sure to remain in a neutral mindset while assessing your failures or lapses. Being observant is crucial to correcting the issue. Imagine you've lost your coat in the subway. It was a source of irritation which caused a fight with your friend when you finally arrived at home. Perhaps you blamed the other person for what happened as a result of the delusional rationale of angry. Spending even two minutes to think about this incident will assist you in understanding how you done something wrong the day. The thought of making a error made you angry and instead of seeing your mistake as simply an error, it caused a lot of distress through the words you spoke to someone that whom you cherish. The practice of this kind can be described as a kind of meditation. Being conscious of your actions and feelings helps you to feel less at ease with these. It is clear the areas where you made mistakes and you can prevent doing the same mistakes again or getting distracted by the melodramas of your mind.

Your bedroom should be comfortable and restful. If other aspects of your life get chaos, you'll have an oasis of calm to go back to. If you're in possession of an apartment or rent a place, you should take the extra time to embellish your sleeping areas with consideration. The soothing tones of subdued tone are a great choice. Some hospitals even opt for the cool cucumber walls as a way to soothe patients.

Tips: Stay clear of Sharp lines and bright colors for your bedroom. Patterns and soft tones are the best.

Clean and clutter-free can help you relax and sleep can be a breeze. If there's a large number of items in an area the eyes of your guests are constantly attracted here and there. This is great for the living room however, it can be distracting when you're in your bedroom, and there should be a couple of important decorations that create a sense of comfort but not overly cluttered. Consider a home plant like a ficus, for an even more restful sleep It will release oxygen, which can improve general health.

Although it may appear straightforward, but going to bed dressed in clean, fresh clothing with a spotless bedroom, and with fresh sheets at the correct time, can make a huge of difference in the way you feel upon waking up next morning. Like the morning routine the evening routine should not be awe-inspiring but it must be systematic and conducive to a calm mindset. It is time to turn off your day-to-day routine when you start your evening routine.

Clean, calm, and serene is your motto.

Chapter 4: Power On Your Morning Routine

"The world changes for each day this is a gift from God, and every man must believe that they are renewed each and every day." Baal Shem Tov. Baal Shem Tov

You will awake with a glow in your eyes. The tenderness of joy that oozes from your chest. The softness of a blanket hugs you while you rise with a springy step. Are you familiar with the scent of Spring, when the last snows of winter melt out, and the plants and flowers are just beginning to grow? This is what we call the early morning. It is the nature of things to be circular. From winter through Spring Autumn to Spring The years continue. Also, a day starts with the spring's vital qualities. When you wake up from the sleep of winter's sleep and advancing through the seasons as a flower that is opening overflowing with fruit, dumping its bounty onto the earth before it goes back to its dormancy.

Be always awake and with a goal. If you don't have a sincere and deep reason for being alive it is just a matter of wasting your time in this Earth. Certain things are interesting to you, some annoy you, but there's no meaning to any thing until you realize the reason you're here. The ultimate meaning of your existence is not something that can be forced. You must discover it. It is entirely in your own hands if you'll look for it. When you discover this element which is like a dedication to God, you'll be in the path you supposed to take. Each person's journey is not exactly the same, but the purpose of our work is always driven with love. If we don't have this passion, there's nothing that thrills our hearts. Choose what you are passionate about to do, and be always looking for more life-giving time to explore and experience it.

Ten golden rules that will make you smile when you wake up:

1. Find an inspiring reason to awake.

2. Take a deep breath and put a Smile across your face.

3. You will wake up at the exact time every throughout the day.

4. Recharge your batteries through music.

5. Get yourself into the ideal time for breakfast.

6. Be Positive.

7. Take a good night's rest.

8. Take care of yourself.

9. Think about how you can create a wonderful day for yourself.

10. Make a decision.

Find a reason that is compelling enough to get up.

The very first stage to have a pleasant beginning of the day is to wake up with a goal.

It's part of your quest to discover that one thing that is truly meaningful for you. If you're aware of the things you are passionate about It will become normal for you to put your attention on it and be satisfied. If you're not certain of the path you're supposed to take in your life look within your soul for the little matters that are important to you. Make sure you are loyal to your parents, as well as your kids. In the toughest of relationships, someone is able to honor their parents simply because they've given him his life. Pets can be a friend to the soul.

Being awake early in the morning and having the responsibility to feed the hungry pets is inspiring. The unconditional love that you get from your pet will be more than enough to reward you.

Smile and open your eyes. Smile to your face.

Before opening your eyes, be grateful to God for the blessings you have received and smile. Take a moment to stretch your muscles and fix your eyes to the very first lighting source you notice light shining through your window or the the constant brightness of an LED bulb. Light destroys darkness. Take a moment to soak in the power that eliminates doubt and anxiety. Be aware that the invisible and visible energy waves of light are transferring to the skin of your body! Let your mind be flooded with positive energy.

Wake up at the same time throughout the throughout the day.

Be consistent with your sleeping habits isn't only very practical but also very beneficial for your health. The best way to avoid tiredness is to rise immediately after you wake up when you lie down. There is a tendency to stay in the cozy confines of your mattress at least a few minutes after you have opened your eyes. It is a thought that you'll have a better sleep however, in actuality it is a sign that you are sleepy. The alarm's sound should alert your body to go back into your bed. You can tell yourself that if you want to get more sleep then you'll head to bed earlier.

Recharge your batteries by listening to music.

Light and sound are the two fundamental physical laws of nature. They are extremely effective. The music you listen to affects your body the moment it is heard. It's more powerful than drugs or medication, but safe and intuitive. An enchanting song will enchant people to the point at which it feels like you are floating across the sky with the melodious and gentle music. Music is a natural, powerful source of energy. Songs that soothe are a great way in lulling a child to sleep. Songs of love cause young hearts to join to their beautiful melodies. Music that is lively and has the beat of a drum can be a great approach to get your mind and body energized at the beginning of your day.

Get yourself into the ideal routine for your morning.

If you're not already waking up at the time you would like to could, then you might consider putting yourself in a personal boot camp in which you'll be pushed to get in form. Set your alarm for an hour earlier than usual, and then you end up hitting the snooze option and resenting that you aren't able to accomplish it. Make a plan to approach the situation more carefully. Start your day 5 minutes earlier than you normally do. It's not noticeable however, if you keep to wake up 5 minutes earlier throughout the day, within about a week or so, you'll be able to effortlessly transition to a productive and efficient day.

Be Positive.

The world is filled with opposing forces. The whites and blacks as well as sweets and sours are everywhere, and in every aspect. Recognize that there are bad things to be found but don't keep them from yourself. Instead, enjoy what's beneficial. Be aware of what you possess instead of your lack of it. There are many positive exercises that encourage the development of positive thoughts. If you feel trapped by a friend or family member near to you in your daily life it is likely that you are disapproving of the way they conduct themselves. It is possible that you don't like this particular behavior, but instead think about how the presence of this person within your life can enrich you. Thank God for the those who care about them. Always have reason to be grateful!

Rest enough.

The power went out in the night. You now need to recharge at full power. A good night's sleep is more likely if you get started on your evening routine around 10:00 PM. When you reach 10:30, you've completed the routine in preparation to go for a peaceful sleep. 7 to 8 hours is the ideal energetic effect. The shorter timeframe will cause you to get tired, and the more is likely to make you tired.

Do not be harsh with yourself.

Enhancing yourself is not an act of winning or losing. Be the very best you can be. There are days when you're bound to fall off the path of your ideal breakfast routine. Stressful events can greatly affect our sleep routine, and so could social interactions that extend into the late midnight hours. If you notice yourself sleeping later, falling down and moody or avoiding your routine totally, don't worry. Accept the fact that you are guilty. Human beings are just that. Your routine can assist you over the long term even if you skip the occasional day. Make these times an opportunity to learn notice the differences in the way you feel as you stick to your routine precisely as opposed to when you're off the track. You will be inspired to take advantage of the results in the coming days!

Find out how you can help make the day unforgettable.

There are days that have a lot of tasks to be done. Other weekends are getaways. These are special moments in that make up our lives. Every day offers us the chance to give back to others. Try to show kindness. Every day, you should think about the places you'll go to and with whom you'll be meeting. Find something you can look towards. Consider ways to do something thoughtful. The one thing you can do is become an integral part of your day life. It will tie your lives by using a needle as the thread of compassion.

Chapter 5: Your New Morning Routine System

The Body

"Fitness involves far more than just exercise. It's the catalyst that can bring about positive changes, and it influences every part of your daily life." Amanda Russell Amanda Russell

A body that's loose where it is flexible and loose where it is supposed to be tight, can become an unwieldy burden to carry around. In pain, heavy and susceptible to sickness You spend time and energy merely ignoring the signs of issues which are more than superficial. Your body no longer carries your weight and it is carried by you an enormous burden.

Wouldn't it be nice to have your body to be a benefit for your life? An engine that is well-oiled and does its job efficiently? It isn't just to those who have lots of spare time or expensive gym memberships. The right to exercise is a human need and is a crucial aspect of a healthy lifestyle. Even the most literary of people can benefit by having a well-balanced and healthy body. The least they can do is people who strive to be attractive and powerful because of a myriad of reasons such as winning in their favorite sport, or even looking stunning to impress a potential partner.

There's no such thing that is more frustrating than not having time to exercise. Are you aware of Barrack Obama's daily morning routine in his time as president? According to top tips (and probably his own sense of) the president knew that physical activity is a key element in being healthy, which then led to an effective decision-making. If the world's top leader can find time for a short exercise routine in the early morning, it is likely that everyone else has time to do it too.

The biggest obstacle to overcome is not a lack of time or endurance, but absence of motivation. A majority of people have experienced the pain of running an extended run and feeling exhausted and weak at the finish. Running can be fun, however it's generally not a great start for people who haven't gotten into routine of exercising. Begin by introducing yourself to high-intensity aerobics. Begin by doing jump in jacks. The blood flow will increase fast, and then you'll be able to rest and complete the number of repetitions you feel comfortably without extending yourself to the limit.

Easy Start-Up Work Out

There are thousands of exercises that you can do. Here's an example of beginners' workout of 15 minutes. routine.

1. 2 Minutes Stretching. Fold forward. Side to Side. Neck Stretches. Back stretches.

2. 5 Minutes Jumping Jacks. (cardio)

3. 5 Minutes Crunches. (30 repeated 10)

4. 2 Minute Push-Ups (5 sets of 10 repetitions))

5. 1 Minute Cool Down. Again stretching. Relaxation.

What ever your fitness routine Include some cardiovascular exercise. Researchers have conducted hundreds of research studies about the advantages of higher blow flow through aerobic exercise. Anything that makes your heart moving is cardio workout such as biking as well as swimming and running.

Find a way to do your exercise You are at ease to switch between different types of exercise particular days of each week. Interval training is a method that involves intense exercises over shorter intervals, followed by low intensities in a alternating sequence. Heart rate is increased drastically when you engage in most intense exercises, and it remains high even after the shift is to a more relaxed movement. The results you get from an intense cardio workout within a fraction of the time. Training intervals is an excellent option for those who aren't yet able to build the endurance. The short and intense exercises can help you build your strength on your way to reaching more advanced goals in fitness. It's also an excellent alternative for an early morning workout as it's very energetic and can be completed in a brief time time and without the need for particular equipment.

Yoga is another form of exercise that is gaining immense popularity with good reason. Yoga is a regular practice that helps keep the body fit and beautiful. People who regularly practice yoga in the course of aging will experience a more graceful aging process, and will experience lesser pains and discomforts. Instead of raising your heart rate, yoga is a great way to stretch your legs and also strengthens your muscles.

There are numerous new variations to this Indian practice. Some are more fast-paced than slow. However, the most common aspect of yoga is to move in harmony with breath. The sun salutation is a starting point of the yoga cycle across a range of yoga styles. Start by putting your arms into the air. Breathe while you bend slowly and straighten your legs. As you inhale, lift your head to the same place. Inhale, and then move to a pushup and then lift your chest upwards while inhaling. Then bend down in an oblique triangle and breathe deeply for five times. Bring your feet closer then rise and back to the original position in the exact pattern. You can do this by breathing in and out with every movement. Then you have completed Surya Namaskar, or Sun Salutation.

Another exercise technique that you could try is to repeat one exercise, like crunches, 15 minutes every day then spending the following day working out a new exercise including squats or squats. This will take exactly the same amount of time. The focus is on a specific part of your body each week, and you'll choose to do seven workouts for every day. The muscles will also have an opportunity to rest through this technique, and the body gets toned throughout each week. Example: Monday crunches, Tuesday jumping jacks, Wednesday weightlifting, Thursday squats, Friday lunges, Saturday planks, Sunday leg raises. Monday: crunches... and then repeat

There's nothing too difficult about exercising However, if you're worried that you're not performing these exercises correctly, think about buying an instructional book that has clear pictures or visiting the web to find a myriad of videos and websites dedicated to routines for fitness.

Be sure to keep your exercise routine well-balanced.

Excessive exertion can wear you down before your workday has began. The right amount of exertion will provide you with an energy boost and a glow of well-being.

What should you eat to nourish the body and tongue

A billboard on the side of the road depicts a happy face, a sparkling bottles of soda on his arm and a golden sheen of fries, which is intoxicatingly shining. However, what is visually appealing and taste great must also serve a objective actual nutrition. Food is often promoted to please our senses of taste alone. There is little consideration given to nutrition as well as, in fact, the manufacturers know that flavor, rather than nutrition is the main factor that sells their products for the majority of people.

Making meals at home using fresh and natural ingredients is the most effective way to prepare eating a nutritious food. It is easy to know what's inside the food you consume since you're purchasing the ingredients, and then making your perfect salad, or nutritious soup. If you achieve your objective of getting earlier in the morning, you'll have extra time for cooking.

Healthy, high-energy breakfast is sure to get you moving and help you perform up to speed until late afternoon. Food preparation can are as quick as 5 minutes.

Some of the most nutritious breakfast options the process take 15 minutes. Certain food items take more time and labour-intensive to make.

Meal 1 Oatmeal and raisins baked in the oven and a glass with milk as well as an orange

The ingredients for baking oatmeal are:

3 Cups Oats

3/4 cup Brown Sugar

2 tablespoons baking powder

Pinch of Salt

Pinch of Cinnamon

2 Eggs

1 Cup milk

1/4 Cup butter

1/4 Raisins

Instructions: Preheat the oven to 350°F. Blend oats with dry ingredients. Mix liquid ingredients together in separate bowl. When thoroughly mixed, mix into Oats. Pour into the pan you have prepared and bake for about 30 minutes or until it is set.

Meal 2 Five fruits salad, toast made of whole wheat as well as a glass of milk

Ingredients for Five Fruit Salad:

2 apples

1 orange

1 pomegranate

1 bunch of red grapes

2 bananas

Topping:

Yogurt

Sugar from coconut

Instructions: Chop apples and bananas. Remove the grapes from their stems, and cut off seeds from the pomegranate. Peel an orange and take out seeds, if needed. Mix all the fruits together, before topping with coconut sugar and yogurt mix.

Meal #3 Pancakes made of multigrains served with honey and the glass of apple juice

Ingredients for Multigrain Pancakes:

1 Cup wheat flour

1/2 cup rice flour

1 cup of Oat flour

1/4 cup ground Flax Seeds

1 tablespoon baking powder

1 cup Milk

1 Egg

3 tablespoons of sugar

1 tablespoon Vegetable Oil 1 tablespoon Vegetable

Pinch of Salt

Instructions Make dry and liquid ingredients in separate bowls before combining. Place the batter in the nonstick pan and form small-sized pancakes. Cook until the pancakes are golden crispy all sides. Serve with honey.

Meal #4 Meal #4 Nut muffins with whole grain with baked grapefruit and glasses of tea with green

Ingredients for Whole Grain Nut Muffins:

1 cup butter melted

1 cup of brown sugar

2 eggs

1/2 cup milk

1/2 teaspoon vanilla extract

1 teaspoon of almond extract

2 cups flour made from whole wheat

2 tablespoons baking powder

1/4 cup cashews

1/2 cup walnuts

Salt and a pinch

Directions: Mix sugar and butter and then mix all the remaining ingredients in the bowl of a large. Make the batter and place it in an oven-proof muffin pan. Bake at 400* for 20 to 25 minutes.

Meal #5: 2 eggs hard-boiled and homemade Granola Bars. glass of milk

Ingredients for Homemade Granola Bars:

4 cups of oats

1 cup Coconut Flakes

1 1/2 cups of chunky peanut butter 1 1/2 cups chunky peanut

1 cup raw sugar

1 cup of molasses

1 teaspoon Sunflower seeds

1 cup flax seed

1 tablespoon chopped walnuts

Instructions: Toast the oats and coconut in a warm oven. Put all ingredients into the pot of a large size and cook until sugar dissolves and slighty thinned. Place in a baking dish and allow it to set.

After you've incorporated a quick fitness session and a energized breakfast to your routine it's best to shower when you're done eating. The shower will wash off the sweat that you've accumulated from your workout routine, and stay awake. However, before opening the hot water tap think about taking a cool shower for the health benefits it offers.

Showers with hot water definitely provide warm sensations as well as comfort. However, once you get out of the bath you're done. However cold showers may be an extreme shock as they can be difficult to bear at first however there's nothing like it to the fresh and rejuvenated sensation you'll feel when you're completed.

It's not a secret that drinking cold water can be a great solution to soothe a tired head.

Tensions can be tamed and it is possible to get in touch with your emotions, and handle your emotions in a way that is appropriate. The anger seems to flow through the drain when it is squelched. It also wakes the lazy out of your. You'll be more prepared than you've ever been to be active after taking a shower. Your feeling of alertness the result of a change in body temperature. The temperature of a warm shower is near your body's temperature or about 100. Cold water bathing in contrast can range from 30-60. Cold signals to the body to stay in your homeostasis as well as to get warm. While at the same time you trigger an immune system that can help combat diseases. The cold water instantly boosts your blood circulation and could help your body reduce fat. Like the exercise routine, showering increases the amount of endorphins produced. A workout with taking a refreshing shower can lead to great success.

If you're still wanting to experience the pleasure of a hot shower, you can try an assortment. Beginning with hot water will have the most effective cleansing effects. The dirt and oil are rapidly dissolving, while the pores your skin are opened. After just a few minutes in warm water, change your faucet to cool. The pores of your skin will tighten to reduce the appearance of blemishes. This provides a general good result on the skin. The water should be kept cold for minimum 90 seconds in order for maximum benefits from taking a shower with cold water.

Just by making a small alteration to your daily routine and you'll be able to relax as well as prevent illnesses and possibly even lose fat. It's uncomfortable after waking up to taking a shower may only last a few minutes, however the benefits you'll experience will soon be apparent which will make you healthier and happier in the longer term.

After you leave your bathroom to the bedroom, you'll need to wash your clothes, especially if you're feeling chilled. Your clothes send a direct signal to all those you encounter about the type you're. Making sure you are careful with your dress choice lets people feel that you're meticulous dedicated, efficient, and diligent. Spend your additional time to select outfits that reflect something about you. An attractive personality can be portrayed through bold, vibrant colors and patterns. Morality is portrayed through traditional attire and a keen care with your shoes and accessories communicates everything about your background, from the culture of origin to the style you prefer.

Never let your clothes depict you as careless. There is no need to possess an amazing fashion sense or a million-dollar closets to demonstrate that you are concerned about others by placing your best foot as well as socks, shoes, and even your pants.

TIP: If you tend to dress in simple, functional clothing, it's an ideal idea to buy some of the same clothes in different hues. Find a flattering outfit will take time. If you are certain that a particular design appeals to you, keeping a variety of styles within your wardrobe will guarantee that you'll always are prepared for which outfit to choose.

Many people who have a busy schedule prefer to choose their outfits at night. This makes dressing easy. You've got your clothes laid out and are ready to go. Transfer from the shower to your room, and after just a couple of minutes, you'll be ready to walk to the exit.

Concentrating on the overall appearance and health of your body can give you lots of confidence you did not know that you had. The fitness routine can give you the healthy glow you desire and will add the color of your skin with the increased blood flow you feel. It's not going to happen overnight However, when you get started with the routine of exercising you will notice your body becoming healthier and attractive. Your stamina and strength will increase which allows you to perform other physical tasks and also makes it easier to work for extended durations of time or even with your computers. Flexibility and overall strength helps to prevent pain and aches. A healthy diet is the final piece of the overall health image. What you eat is your health Fresh, nutritious food choices make for a healthy well-nourished person.

Chapter 6: Your New Morning System The Mind

"A positive mindset triggers an unintended cycle of positive thoughts as well as events and results. It acts as a catalyst, and can lead to extraordinary outcomes." Wade Boggs. Wade Boggs

Our bodies are made up of these three fundamental parts: the body, mind and the spirit. Many people know the importance to keep your body in excellent shape, even if they struggle to time adhering to the healthy way of life. However the demands of our brains are different and can be difficult to figure out what you need to take to ensure your mental wellbeing. With a bit of knowledge, that it's really not difficult at all. By following a few simple rules, you can make a huge difference to your mental wellbeing and help maintain a healthy mindset that permits you to live your life in the best way possible.

Nobody really wants to think negatively. However, life's challenges interfere with an optimistic outlook When negative thinking begins, it can be an endless cycle. The negative thoughts can cause people to talk negatively, which can be damaging and separating connections with friends as well as family. Problems that arise result in more bad feelings as well as more negative feelings. It keeps going as if it were a mill. So long as there's negative energy, it will keep spinning. Resolving to end this routine is crucial to lead a an enjoyable life.

Certain methods, such as breathing or meditation help calm an anxious mind. Positive affirmations are an successful method for maintaining the peace and tranquility of your mind. Although the affirmations might appear false at first however, they provide the most effective way of creating faith. Let go of doubts about these methods and give them a serious test. It is likely that you will be free of old, dull ideas and feel refreshed and optimistic.

Breathing Exercises

Breathing. Out and in. Out and in. At times of stress an airy rush is released in a loud sound. When we are in a state of excitement when our chest is tense, it accelerates its movements, and oxygen richly circulates through our body and brightens eyes. In the midst of a panic, sorrow, until death your breath is a continuous force we never notice. Our lungs, which are constantly working, contract and expand to create this graceful sequence. The breath we take never ceases to amaze us. Yet, we struggle to appreciate its power and make use of it. The breathing exercises draw our attention to our constant breathing. They help us listen to our breath. They also teach us to be aware of its subtle processes. If we can understand this procedure, we will know how to breath for peace as well as breathe to improve health and to breathe with happiness.

Most of the time, we be aware of our breathing when there's an issue. A swollen nose makes breathing impossible by the nostrils. Chest pains make every breath an effort. The smell of toxic fumes makes us reduce our breaths and avoid breathing toxic chemicals. What happens for the 99percent of the time in which we breathe regularly breathing for life? Most of the time, we are deep breaths, getting little or no oxygen they are able to get from their surroundings. Making a conscious effort to pay attention to the breath, and learning about how to breathe fully, not necessarily in a deep way however, filling your diaphragm properly with plenty of air makes our minds and bodies better functioning.

The art of breathing with the diaphragm

The human body is a complicated system which lets us breathe. Our noses and mouths have the pathways that let air enter into the respiratory tract of our upper airways. The larynx, pharynx and trachea go through and the air is able to reach the lung. The bronchial tube distributes the air in the lungs, and exchange carbon dioxide with oxygen. If the lungs are filled the chest and the ribs expand in a condition. The muscle located right below the lungs is known as the diaphragm. When you breathe correctly it works together with our lung to flush the air.

You can tell that your breathing is working effectively through your diaphragm by doing the simple act of lying down on a rug or bed and put an object on your abdomen area. Relax in a normal way. If the book is rising dramatically in a tumbling motion then your diaphragm has expanded. If the book moves only just a bit, you'll be aware that your breathing is shallow. The chest is rising and expanding more than the stomach. Breathing in the chest demands greater energy, and also is less able to absorb oxygen. Begin by breathing until the stomach is rising and falling. Learn what it is like to feel and how it feels. You will also get comfortable breathing using the diaphragm.

Breathing using diaphragms isn't an actual practice, but is the right method to take in oxygen and release air at the highest level of your body's capacity. It is an antecedent to many various breathing techniques as well as a method to achieve the best well-being. Try to breathe the same way.

After you've figured out how you breathe through your diaphragm muscles, you'll be able to rest assured that you're getting closer to improving your well-being, and you can start testing different breathing methods to incorporate into your daily routine.

Method #1 Deep Breathing

It is a simple breathing method. It isn't to be ignored. Breathing deeply can be calming and can help stabilize your mood.

Step 1: Remain in a comfy posture and breathe comfortably.

Step two: Begin inhaling deeply.

Third step: Keep your breath for about 1 or 2 minutes.

Step 4: Inhale gently.

Step five: Repeat until relaxed.

Method #2 Kapalbati Yogic Breathing

Kapalbati is a renowned breathing technique, which originated from the Indian subcontinent. The word translates roughly to the bright-faced breathing. It implies that the technique of breathing increases the happiness and wisdom. The mechanism behind it is to contract the stomach muscles when exhaling to ensure that breathing is effortless.

Step one: Sit on your knees or sit in a chair, keeping the back straight.

Step two: Inhale deeply.

Third step: exhale. When you exhale the stomach muscles, you should pull them towards the back as much as you can. Keep pulling your stomach back until you have exhausted all the air taken out.

Fourth step: You'll immediately inhale after having removed all the air.

Five steps: Repeat this the 20 sets in sets.

The method completely cleanses the lungs completely of air and carbon dioxide completely. This method allows the highest amount of oxygen into the body, which improves circulation. It's thought to stimulate the digestive system of the body and aid in weight loss and weight loss.

Method #3 Nasal Inhale/Oral Exhale Breathing

Breathing in through your nostril and then out of the mouth is a popular way to get rid of cramps. It's also a great technique to reduce the negative effects.

Step 1. Breathe through the nostrils.

Step 2: Take a deep breath for three to four seconds.

Step 3: exhale slowly by mouth.

Step 4: Repeat as desired.

In this manner, breathing will help ease pain in your body. Use this technique to relax your body. the following visualization: As you exhale through your nose, the air will feel warmer. Imagine your breathing as cool blue flow of positive energy flowing towards the inside of you. The more hot breath it is exhaled can be imagined in red, representing bad feelings negative emotions, anger, and negativity disappearing from your body. It will be easier and positive at the end of your session.

Being Grateful

An unexpected flower in your front yard or a text note from a person that you believed had forgotten about or a tasty food... It's a matter of many small and insignificant things that are worth celebrating and lift us up incrementally. As a group of birds carrying each just a bit of weight, they help us climb and enable us to fly. Small and large they are, and there are plenty of benefits to living a life. Giving thanks to the positive aspects of your life will awaken the awareness of what you truly are able to enjoy. This helps you get rid of the thoughts of material things that make people feel that they never get enough, and must work harder till... you reach a day comes that doesn't come. Instead, take a step back for a moment and take a look at how beautiful your life has become. You are blessed with people who cherish your. The things you cherish. Beauty of nature. Art.

Be grateful as aspect of your daily routine. Do not just write down things on your list consider writing your gratitude on the paper. Make a spiral bound or a notebook for your gratitude journal. Within this journal, you should take about 4-5 minutes every day to reflect on the things you're grateful for and the reasons. Pick three things. When you start there will be plenty of reasons that you can be grateful for without hesitation. When you write daily entries it can be difficult to believe that you've run out of thoughts. But this isn't an exercise in creativity, even though you might be utilizing an element of creativity when writing. The focus is on what you've got and the things you cherish in your life. Repeating these things over and over is great for reminding your self every day that these things matter to you. Lover's say, 'I can create a book on my love'.

An example of a thank-you journal entry

April 3rd

This morning I woke to birdsong. I'm so happy that it's finally spring. It is so nice to sleep by the window. The breeze is already releasing this warm, refreshing smell and some blooms have begun to flower. One of the reasons I enjoy Spring more than just the beauty of nature and the fact that everybody seems to be happy taking a break from the house, and having fun with one another.

I'm thankful to John for his excellent grades on his Chemistry test. I was extremely worried the student was behind in his work However, I'm sure that I helped him get to where he was. I am proud of him for the fact to see him succeed. I'm sure he's got the right mindset up his sleeve, and if is focused and is diligent, he will be successful with whatever he decides to accomplish. I like that he's taking on a challenge by learning Chemistry instead of picking the easier option.

I'm particularly grateful for the brand new café that was opened in the area of our office. This may appear to be something minor however, I look for the fresh bread and soup that they offer in the lunch time. This makes me feel more relaxed working knowing that I'll have some good food as well as a moment to unwind before starting work once more. In the past, I packed lunch or going to an alternative location further from me, however I can conserve time in eating at home, and it's healthier and tasty!

There are a myriad of reasons you can write about that you are grateful for. If you'd like to more, you could write long elaborate reasons for your feelings. It will be a note of the best aspects of your life or when you're feeling down, you'll access it and experience an instant boost of mood when you remember these events.

Be grateful and you learn valuable lessons in everyday life. Most likely, you've heard this message previously, but in the event you've lost it, it's about being present and valuing the things you've got.

The act of writing each day provides you with an opportunity to set the tone for your day. Have you heard that saying, "You don't realize what you've got until you've gone through it? If you're not grateful, the saying definitely rings true. If you're happy, you're aware of what you've been blessed with that you are grateful for, and you do not let through it only to think about that it's gone.

Tips: Do this exercise to feel grateful for your overall health. We often are only aware of certain parts of our body only when they're in pain. If they're in good functioning condition, we tend to do not notice the problem. Take a look at a toothache, backache or a broken toe. Concentrate on these areas of your body that perform well. For example: You may have"a reverse backache'. Feel the sensations of your spine and back. The sensations are all there, the muscles are moving in a proper manner. The muscles feel great and are in good shape. They are fit and healthy. The practice of this kind will get you in touch to the physical well-being of your body.

Meditation

Yoga yogis seated at the summit of a mountain, his legs crossed, a calm expressions grace the lips and shut eyes... He is breathing slow, being a statue in motion that is immune to winds and rain. The image of meditation an image of a particular sort of contemplation. The masters of yoga and the boddhisatvas, who are boddhis the entire day and evening at idyllic locations, retreating to their own inner world. Although it may be difficult to be in this kind of posture, but the practice of meditation can be extremely helpful for everyone. It doesn't require you to climb to the top of a mountain simply some quiet space. It's not necessary to fight winds and rain, however, more pragmatic obstacles like doubt and uncertainty.

Meditation has been around for as long as the human race. In every nation and society, people have sought refuge in the quiet areas of their mind where they seek to find peace. Meditation is different in its external ways. The most effective method of meditation is by sitting cross-legged, and close your eyes. You can also try other kinds of meditations to choose from, such as the spoken and moving meditations. The repetition of the same phrase repeatedly will bring your mind to a calm and single-pointed experience. Certain meditations focus on taking a breath, while others include specific imagery and or religious symbolism. It is important to find the right meditation for your needs so that you are able to practice it continuously. The practice of meditation frequently will certainly provide an increase in clarity. However, consistent practice is vital for a significant improvement on your own personal development.

The essence of meditation, as it is called is a way to can help you clear your mind. It allows you to experience the state of being in a completely different way that may be accompanied by feelings of relaxation, bliss as well as lucidity.

Meditation on the Breath

For a start on with the simplest exercises, begin by sitting in a straight back. It is possible to sit on your knees, in a lotus pose as well as in a solid back chair. The way you sit is entirely your choice, however ensure that you keep a the correct posture. This lets the chest open and allows sufficient air flow through the lung. It is advised to be in a calm spot, for instance the bedroom when nobody is present or in a quiet place outside in the yard or patio. Do not sit in areas where there are people who are talking or creating noise, and worse is if they stare at you while meditating! When you've located the perfect spot and are sitting in a straight position then you are able to start the process of contemplation.

Shut your eyes and take note of the breath. It is a different approach to the breathing methods we talked about in the past. The best way to breathe is not trying to modify or regulate the breathing pattern that is normal. It is best to take note of. Take a deep breath and then feel the breath entering your nostrils through your throat, to your lungs, and deep into the lung. The breath stays in your chest for only just a few seconds. Concentrate to the breath. When you exhale naturally you will feel your breath rise into your chest.

Then, it will return through your throat, then out of your nostrils. Within a millisecond time the breath will stay out until you inhale once more. Keep watching.

In the beginning, you'll be able to follow your breath effortlessly. The mind is captivated by the unique experience of tracking your breathing. After just several breaths, the curiosity will diminish as other thoughts come to mind. The thoughts of your physical condition such as hunger, pains as well as posture will spring into your mind while you are sitting. Then, more complex thoughts come into play on the horizon people you'll be meeting when you've finished your meditation or talking about or recall of previous events. You'll soon realize that you've totally forgotten about your breathing and you're riding through the thrilling ride of your brain. In just a couple of moments, your mind has changed to a completely other issue. It is the time to learn how to truly meditate. Do not be apprehensive about getting off track it's common and normal for your brain to work such a way. Keep your mind glued to your breathing. When thoughts start to creep into your mind, be aware of them however, let them go without judgement. If you are pulled in this manner and the other way, continue the focus on the breath. As you continue to meditate by doing this your mind will become more relaxed and easy to get. Your thoughts will be focused on nothing else but the steady, slow movement of the air in your body, and out. It is possible to experience an intense sense of clarity and reflection, or a sensation of calm and peace. Every person responds differently to meditation and at their personal time. If you are feeling anything during your the meditation process, be grateful and with no judgement.

Open-Eye Meditation

A different type of meditation can be done when you stare at an object while keeping your eyes open. Sometime, artwork and images with circular symmetry are the focal point. Others choose images of religion which are significant to them like images that depict Christ and Buddha. The object could appear to be a representation of the burning flame of a candle, or even a sparkling drop of dew in a grass piece. Whatever object you pick to reflect about, make sure you place it at a minimum of an arm's distance away from your. Pay attention to the object with full concentration and total concentration. Be sure to blink, however continue to look in the exact direction towards the object you have chosen. Be sure to observe it with attention without missing one single thing.

Be sure to keep looking at it with no hesitation, and refrain from having a mental picture or forming opinions about the object you're looking at. You should not be able to recall details regarding the object or think about possible interactions. All your attention should be put towards observing it. Absolutely nothing else than what it is. It is exactly as it was. If you do get distracted from the object, and then turn away and then return to it the same way you came back. If your thoughts begin to go free, control them and revert back to your practice.

Keep meditating for a predetermined time and/or until you are completely relaxed and influenced by your practice. In the majority of meditations during a period of a few moments or minutes, you may struggle to get into the state of meditative while sorting out internal and external clutter.

Concerns about money, thoughts of conversations or a more pressing work due to a date... Whatever the thoughts that pop up Let them go. The moment is not the time to dwell on those thoughts. It is possible that they are good or meaningful however in this time during this practice, only the object you are focusing on is significant to you. When you're contemplating for 15 minutes, then you will definitely spend those fifteen minutes focusing. Other thoughts and concepts which you have let go of do not go away forever and will still be around after you've completed the meditation. Continue to gaze at the subject with all your strength and enjoy the bliss of being single-pointed.

Chakra Meditation

The benefits of meditation are particularly valued by Eastern traditions. Hinduism as well as spiritual belief systems as well state that there are seven chakras or energy centers, which make up the body's subtle structure. These chakras are located along a straight line, and are that is in alignment with the body's spine. The initial chakra is located near the base of the spine. the highest or final chakra lies above the head. Each of these chakras has a specific purpose and a distinct domain of control over the individual. The lower chakra is devoted to essential needs of the person such as nutrition and shelter. The chakra in the throat refers to the expression of self. As with many organs in the body, chakras work together to create a perform. When all of them are functioning well, a person is in good health.

It is thought to be home to a hidden energy which is located in the apex of the spine, until it is awakened. The awakening of this energy will lead to greater wisdom and knowledge. This energy increases with frequent mindfulness and concentration on every chakra inside the body.

If you're not aware of chakras and their philosophy This kind of practice is extremely beneficial for those who are just beginning their journey and even advanced one. It is a active meditation that is not merely paying attention to a specific item, for example breathing or an object. The practice involves sounds or mantras recited mentally, and focusing the mind on specific areas of the body, and also its associated chakra. The chakra that is the first one has the sound "Lam". This sound is spoken by bringing attention towards the point in the middle of the spine, and observing the energy circle that is there. Many people assign different colors to every chakra. Focus on the tone, hue, as well as the place of the chakra for a few minutes or the count of 30, depending on your preference. The next chakra is over that and the sound it makes is called "Vam.". Make the sound slowly, and visualize it pulsing out through the chakra's area. Keep repeating the sound over a period of time. The third chakra is located in the stomach region. The sound of this chakra is "Ram". The chakra is believed to be the home of confidence in self-esteem and abilities. The second chakra is the heart chakra. It is the one that is the one that governs compassion and love. The sound it makes is "Yam". The neck chakra produces the 'Ham' sound as well as the one in the area of the brow includes the sound 'Om. The highest and final chakra lies just below the top of the head. rather than emitting the sound of the head, it emits silence.

In the practice of chakra meditation, each zone is targeted during a limited time. The fundamentals and areas of each chakra may be discovered in a variety of publications on the subject or through an internet research. What is most important regarding this practice is that a sensation of increasing energies that you feel while you step one up the scale of chakras. It is an experience of increased awareness and development within the chakra's areas. When you focus on the chakra of your heart it is easy to feel your heart growing larger with universal love. The crown chakra is a source of knowledge that provides your with universal understanding.

One reason that it's easy to follow the meditation routine is that it is it a lot of fun. It operates in harmony with your thoughts: your thoughts are centered on chakra-related elements and your instinct for speaking will be used in the inner repeating of the mantra.

Integrating 15 minutes of mindfulness to your morning routine is among the greatest things you can make to yourself. At first you might feel that 15 minutes of time is too long to take in, making it difficult to concentrate long enough for your daily meditation. However, after a couple of weeks of consistent practice You may find that you're looking to increase the length of the duration of your practice. Benefits you experience in meditation are vast. Certain tangible advantages such as increased concentration as well as a reduction in irritability and improved ability to concentrate. However, other advantages that meditation can provide are hard to describe. A general feeling of being in space as well as a heightened interest in life and the experience that are more heightened also result when you practice regularly practicing practice of meditation.

Daily Affirmations

In the mirror you can see someone who is nervous, uncertain about himself. You look a bit sluggish and you're not sure the things you'd like and don't know what that you have the ability to make your life into a walk in dream. You aren't. Your lips are parted in a sound, your words bring sparkles to your eyes. The cheeks are brimming with colour, and you'll be able to resist letting the smile dance across your face. "Everything is happy." The words you speak truly. Although you may not think they were sincere as you heard them the message they convey strikes in the heart, and joy radiates.

Positive affirmations are the best illustration of the 'fake it until you can't make it' strategy to help increase your productivity and assured. These are frequently re-used however, few realize how powerful they can be in method.

When someone is insecure, telling her self that she's beautiful could be seen as a parody. There is a temptation to let it go But you'll be returning to the place you began. If you stay with affirmations, then you'll see that they transform your life from within. The message you give to yourself is transmitted through the sounds of your voice. It is absorbed into your ears as well as your brain the message is planted in a plant that grows into a tangible shift within your.

If you are feeling tired and are having a difficult time having focus, it's be difficult to convince yourself that you're the most effective and efficient person that you have ever known. However, those words are not just a nagging feeling in you as well as the opportunity to be exactly what you'd like to become.

There is no limit in the variety of affirmations you can choose to adopt or incorporate into your daily routine. One of the most important questions you should think about do you want the most and the most pressing issues you have to face. Once you have a clear idea of the things you desire you will know which affirmation type is appropriate for you. Certain affirmations are universal and the positive emotions that they bring to your cell. I'm an intelligent, helpful and compassionate, and all that I do is done in love.

Certain affirmations may also be precise. Imagine yourself as an expert in genetic research and studying a disorder. The most important thing you want to accomplish for your professional life is to conduct relevant research in order to discover the cause and treat this condition. It is possible to choose the phrase "I'll find the gene sequence and figure out what I can do to fix this mutation." The goal-oriented declaration outlines precisely what you're trying to achieve and will give you the assurance you need to complete your task and be successful with your work.

The power of affirmations can brighten your life.

I'm gorgeous just how me.

Every person who comes in contact with me learns some thing from me.

I find myself in the stream of life.

Happiness can be a choice.

The most amazing thing that happens that is everywhere.

I'm perfectly healthy. My brain is in top shape. I'm in complete sync with the world around me.

I love being alive.

Confirmations that dispel doubts and anxiety

I am safe.

I am not stopping anyone from being a wonderful individual.

My earnings are growing.

I will not let anything or anyone else, harm me.

I am tolerant of and respectful of different opinions of people regardless of whether I necessarily agree with them.

There is nothing that will cause me to be upset today.

Career-oriented Affirmations

Nobody in the office is the same way as I do.

When I train, I grow.

I'll finish my work three times more quickly than yesterday.

I'm getting on the right path toward successful results.

My profession is a great match for me.

I'm equipped with the knowledge I'll need to achieve my goals.

In as little as 2 minutes, or even 10 minutes during your morning engaging in affirmations that are positive can boost your day. There are a variety of ways of saying your affirmations. First, you can speak direct to yourself, in front of your mirror. Look at yourself in the mirror and repeat the phrase, without rushing, and not too fast. Use a clear, firm voice. If you are embarrassed by others hearing your praises you can lower the volume however, make sure that you speak with a firm voice. An unconvincing, low-pitched voice transmits a message to the world that you do not believe the affirmations you're making. Repeat the affirmation over and over and then repeat a couple of various affirmations. It is possible to memorize the words you'd like to say or even write it down on paper.

TIP: Sticky notes in the mirror or in front of it help you remember to make your affirmations every day. Make them written in colorful marker that is bright and big bold letters.

Another method of doing your daily affirmations is to have them not stated, but rather spoken. This is a great method to do while doing other activities or even when you are dressing or showering. Breathe deeply and repeat your affirmation to yourself. It doesn't matter which place you're at or whom you're in with, your affirmation is like being a secret that is kept. It is possible to feel excited by the powerful story you're affirming to yourself. And you will cherish this as an exclusive knowledge just for you to be aware of.

Another way to utilize your affirmation as a way to counter any negative thoughts that are circulating through your thoughts. It is a way to kick those negative thinking patterns in the event that you can counter them fast and with confidence.

When you hear yourself saying"I'm just too exhausted to prepare breakfast, so I'll skip it. You immediately use the affirmation, 'I'm in a state of unending energy'. When you think you're too exhausted of cooking, you go to another part of your brain and realize that you possess unlimited energy. There is a surge of energy through your body as you say these phrases. Then, suddenly, you feel an energy boost and you're ready to begin cutting. Utilizing this technique throughout your morning routine or whenever you experience an un-empowering feeling, it helps you get in the right direction before negativity is able to take over.

The power of affirmations can be a powerful device in your arsenal that boosts your productivity and energy levels. techniques that comprise an excellent morning routine. If you meditate every morning, adding positive affirmations in addition to it, you're doing the steps necessary for a healthy and positive well-being.

Conditions like depression and anxiety are very grave. These are conditions that could be significantly altered due to the habits we adopt which keep us in a best mental state. It is easy to lose track of, but your mental health isn't as important or different than the physical condition of our body. If you are eating the proper diet and exercises the body responds by achieving optimal functioning and an amazing sensation. It's the same with your mind. If you can put the correct "foods" in your brain and regularly use them You'll feel the blissful feeling of complete health. Both inside and outside.

Your Daily Goals

The way you wish to go in your life is the topic was discussed in the past discussing the reason why you wake up each early morning. It is important to establish an idea of the long-term reason you're here on planet. The things you enjoy doing and how you'll be doing it each day of your existence. Life can be complicated. We want love, friendship satisfaction, spiritual development and success in the material world. In our souls, we feel the desire to express our self as creatively as well as socially by using art mediums or by being part of a larger group.

Our desires and hopes on this earth, however, aren't items we're able to simply go to do.

It's the trip that lasts an entire lifetime. As with a long way to the end, you don't know where you intend to go by just making a decision to travel. The way to get there is by taking a walk. The steps you take this morning are the ones you'll must consider in your early morning routine.

Like you have incorporated your own journal to record what you're thankful to have in your morning routine Start your morning by making a short listing of your goals for the day. Keep in mind that quality over the quantity of things, so decide on what you are able to accomplish during the next 24 hours. There are days when you will face a big task in front of you. Your aim is to finish it to the very best possible level. However, you should include at least two and no over 4 goals for the day. When you've got a task in front of you, think about splitting that goal into smaller parts. Sometimes, writing down the goals down will let you know what you must do this day. If you don't have particular deadlines or schedules before you, there is a chance that you'll cut the time to be lower than the most productive. Everybody needs to rest and rest, but don't allow a single day to go unproductive. If your objectives are straightforward the day before and could be done in a relatively short period of time then excellent. However, don't forget your objectives or just ignore them.

First thing to record when beginning the list of goals for your day is what you intend to accomplish. Are you looking to launch an entirely new venture? Are you looking to create something new, for example writing songs? Are you looking to master some thing? What can you do to enhance the quality of your interactions with people? Consider the thing you'd like to achieve before you come up with a title to your objective in no more than a couple of phrases.

What you need to note down a bullet listing of the things you intend to achieve: it is the "how" to achieve your objectives. This could include specific actions to follow in order to get things accomplished. Consider that you have make some repairs to your house. The list of items you'll need to make is extremely precise. It is necessary to visit the shop and purchase supplies, repair this and paint it before you complete it. The other projects will not require specific steps but will require a variety of factors to ensure your goals are completed. As an example, perhaps you have been looking for an opportunity to get a new job. Your objective on that particular day (and likely for the next few days during your search for a job) is essentially that you find an opportunity to work. Some of your bullet points could include searching for listings on the internet, calling firms, revising your CV to include more details, talking with for a reference from a person to join your search, and other such. A star can be placed beside your bullet points that you think are most important for your goals.

If you choose to set many goals, you can arrange your goals across different areas of your daily life. You should set goals to your professional lifestyle, your personal activities, and even your personal life. There are many who believe that goal-setting is primarily concerned with advancing your career and getting to the top however this isn't the reality. Setting goals for your spouse as well as family relationships could be among the most productive ways to go about it in your daily routine It will help shape your character into a more balanced, gentle human being. If you are experiencing tension and rudeness with people with whom you share a family relationship is the norm, you should make your intention to be more harmonious and make sure you are nice to this individual throughout the day. It is possible to think of something that you would like to convey to them on a particular day, something you truly mean sincere heart. By taking the time to think about these issues will take your relationship to a new step and eliminate the tension of unbalanced interactions.

A mere 10 minutes during the morning to decide the goals you have set is only a tiny portion of your day-to-day routine. These 10 minutes could make the difference between having an amazing, productive and enjoyable day, or an unorganized one.

Once you've written down your day-to-day goals with the paper with a pen, consider what your life would look like after you have achieved your goals. Think about the things you would like to complete. Enjoy the feeling of joy and satisfaction due to their achievement.

Being immersed in the total visualization of the accomplishments will accomplish two things. It inspires you and also sends a message to your mind that it will happen. This will eventually end in a matter of hours, you only need to work hard in order to reach that point. The brain will take this as reality and you'll have the confidence that this will be accomplished, and done within a single day.

If you had a goal of the day was editing the video to get a job. Perhaps it was something that you thought you'd need to accomplish over the course of a couple of days, however you've made the choice to complete it now. No procrastinating, no excuses. The bullet points the way you're working to get your work accomplished. The footage must be uploaded and then rename it. You must then create an appealing intro. You must also incorporate text in an appropriate font to match the footage as well as is simple to read.

Also, you must search for appropriate ambient music that will be used to accompany the video. Then, you'll modify the video as you wish before saving it and then send the video to your client. The title of your goal and bullet points make it simple to arrange yourself. When you've completed your list it will be clear the steps to take and the best way to do it.

As you begin to imagine the finished video the video will be the sequence of events even watching the movie playing before your eyes in a seamless and flawless manner. It will sound the music and see the frame flash through, and experience the emotional impact you would like the video to hold. In your visualisation there will be a glimpse of you clicking the send button, before receiving an email from the client letting you know how satisfied that he was with the project that you've submitted.

If you imagine your objective at its best and create a precise, precise plan for how you'll accomplish your task the next day. If you state 'I'll succeed in my endeavor' you have a lot of room for error and you're not getting the same progress towards the goal than if you began without planning to succeed. You need to have clear straight and precise information about the things you want to achieve. Let's take another scenario. You are planning to do an interview to a local radio station regarding an issue related to human rights that you are passionate about.

The feeling is intense and your heart is brimming over with anger and frustration. There are a couple of heartfelt things that you are constantly running through your thoughts that are important to you. However, you're in the wrong place about who your customer is. The best way to plan for success will look a lot like the usual goal with bullet points. You want to 'Give an Outstanding Interview and Help Educate others'. Making a plan for how to accomplish this can help you plan. Do some investigation.

Perhaps you haven't done any research on the subject at hand, but you're likely to know a good quantity if you're conducting an interview of this kind. Make sure that you are aware of the target audience on the show. Also as well as what other programming are being aired, and which ones are popular and what locations do people tune into the broadcast? If your viewers are from an entirely different culture than yours should make sure you address them appropriately.

The emotions that affect you may sound different than the ones that affect them. Also, you should add a lot of concrete factors to help you succeed this day. Sipping a cup of hot sweetened green tea will calm your throat and improve your voice and make it soft and comfortable. Consider the issues you could be faced with so that they don't shock you as you're broadcasting.

Once you've written everything written down in the paper and pen, you can walk through your completed interview. Pay attention to your voice. yet not overly imposing and empathetic but not too excessively sappy. You can hear yourself giving a thoughtful and imaginative answer to a difficult question and imagine the face of the person you are interviewing, clearly satisfied with your expertise on the subject and your thoughtful understanding of the question.

Imagine getting a call from a person who's seen the program and is congratulating you for an excellent job. Be cautious concerning the picture you imagine against what actually happens. The purpose of this exercise is to build assurance and prepare. It's not always going as planned. However, with your eyes on the table and a plan to do instead of being blindfolded and batting like the child playing the game of pinata. One of the most appealing aspects of life is dealing with the unpredictable. If all things went how you would like all would remain boring and routine. Let whatever comes up gracefully and utilize your own vision of success as a reference for what you can do to respond.

Lifelong Learning

If you were in school during the summer months, you likely ran through the halls and out into the schoolyard, screaming thrilled to have all the hours ahead that were full of joy and completely free from the burdens of homework and examinations. Schoolbooks were scattered around collecting dust, and inviting spiders who would build webs of cobwebs, and sleep in the pages that were yellowed. Fun and friends beckoned your attention, while the rays of warm sun flooded you with pure joy. When you arrived home, by the time you had finished your vacation there was nothing more than a road sign while driving somewhere.

Chapter 7: Your Completed Morning Routine

It's time to leave the house elegant and attractive. There's something special about you which makes you appear charming without even saying a word. Your clean and stylish clothes are hung over your slender body and you've got the stylish appearance of someone who can reach to the top with ease. Once you've mastered the guidelines of your game There is no reason for gruelling attempts or jumbled efforts.

You're aware of exactly what you have to accomplish You have written it on your plan of your daily tasks.

It's it's not because of luck that you've complied with the appropriate steps to fall asleep easily and at a good time. It wasn't just effortless and it was wonderful. The air was filled with sunshine and warmth, grateful to receive a the new day to learn and live.

The morning was a rush of excitement as you jumped out of the couch, thrilled by your morning routine you had planned and eager to go.

Your affirmations for the day flowed naturally from your mouth while you scrubbed the sleepiness of sleep by a mix of suds and soap.

You trust that every word you hear is authentic. Your face gets an unassuming smile, obscuring your deep joy in your heart with a subdued tone. The confidence that you feel in your heart is hotter than the sun. those cold, icy icicles of doubt have been smashed out of your mind long ago.

You are who you really are, and you have an intense love for yourself. You're at the right place You face yourself in a way that is compassionate when you do make mistakes. You are confident that you will never go off-track even if you slip a bit.

Respecting your body's role as the engine which drives you throughout the day. You started the workout. The flow of blood through your veins was a treat and your breath was pure oxygen, with the joy of tasting something special.

If you're ready for breakfast, you were enjoying the task cutting and mixing components of your breakfast. You enjoyed the vegetables and grains you consume not just for their delicious flavor as well as the nutritional value they provide to you.

After a refreshing shower after a refreshing shower, your clothing was all laid out and ready for take off. The soft textures glided over your skin before sliding to the point of adorning your figure and enhancing the appearance of your face. Then, before you left your feet, you laid on a sofa on the side of your space and started with a long breath.

The breathing exercises helped you relax and then you relaxed into your morning ritual. The vision of a blue, clear luminescence ahead of you, the entire energy of love and wisdom. The energy and light you focused on felt like an old comrade, and you were meditating on it was like a treasured trip.

The time that you were in meditation seemed to fly through without a blink. The feeling of being energized and calm was apparent instantly. The experience made writing in the gratitude journal a reflex. It was the same thing that you're grateful for each day, namely being thankful for the good things in the present which has now become an affirmation to the past few months since you started your daily routine that encourages positive thinking. Then you wrote down three additional items you are grateful for, however it would have been possible to write more. Your pen was moved onto a new page and began to sketch out your objectives with calm concentration. You were aware that you'd got lots of commitments ahead of you. However, you picked one task to finish as well as two other goals which you believed that you were able to accomplish. In a logical order you pondered ways you could get the day's tasks accomplished.

Prior to leaving the house before leaving, you checked out something sweet an excellent ebook from your library. The book was not just fun to read, it was also educational as well, and you learned a few facts that you discussed with friends back in your home.

After that, when it was time you left, it was as if you'd finished a full day. It's hard to remember the time where the first day went by, with just one or two hours to before you ate and dressed. Today, you've completed more than in the times before learning how to stay organized.

Chapter 8: Collect Habits

The initial step of this procedure is to accumulate the habits that you'd like to implement in practice. There are some practices that everybody can profit from (which I'll show you) while others only benefit certain individuals.

Let me first explain what I have discovered through Positive Psychology, a branch of research that studies the strengths of individuals as well as communities to enable individuals to flourish and lead happily. The psychologists who study this field have identified the people who are most content to ensure that the rest of us benefit from their model. Each of these positive behavior patterns have been examined in a research study that has been proven to lead to an improvement in the happiness for the subject.

Humans are designed to work out. Consider this the way our ancestors traveled far distances in pursuit of their quarry. They relied on physical endurance and strength to consume food and thus be able to live. Human bodies naturally adjusted throughout the years to the harsh environment which meant that exercise was (and continues to be) fundamental for all of humans. When we think about evolution, it's evident that physical exercise is not an option to enjoy. It's a necessity.

Research suggests fitness requirements vary from individual to person, based on the person's health, age and other factors. As a general rule one should workout for 30 minutes to an hour every day, for 4 five days per week. In this moment it is possible that you think "I am not able to find the time to train for even 30 minutes per day". In this case there are many issues to be addressed.

In the beginning, I think doing exercise early in the day is fantastic, and sometimes even wonderful. It gives you energy and enthusiasm all morning. But, it's true that spending thirty minutes or more of your daily Routine to exercise just for fun isn't for everyone. Therefore, make sure you exercise during your day and also keep in mind that even if you do not have to be at work early, the first thing in the morning can be an ideal time to exercise.

The other aspect to consider is whether to exercise either before or after breakfast. As per toJohn Rowley, the Wellness Director of the International Sports Science Association (ISSA) People who strive at weight loss can benefit by exercising with a full stomach, while those with various fitness goals don't.

In spite of all the preceding considerations regardless of the above considerations, doing a short exercise at the beginning of the day is suggested for all (By this If you've got the opportunity to get outdoors to let the sun shine over your face, go for it! It's so amazing and useful). Based on the age and stage the possibilities are endless:

A five minute stroll in the area

7 minutes of workout. This is a great approach that is packed with a range of exercises for every muscle group. At first, it's very challenging. You are welcome to download the application. (http://well.blogs.nytimes.com/2013/05/0 9/thescientific7minuteworkout/?_r=0)

5 minutes of warming exercise (including stretching, running and jumping. For those who train for sports like basketball, football or tennis will be able to relate to this)

Rebounding. Rebounding has grown more and more popular. In essence, it's all about jumping and falling on a tiny trampoline.

It is important to keep your heart beating and blood flowing which is why you should choose the workout that you feel most comfortable with and take it to the next level. Also, if you're able to get connected to nature when exercising this will help make the beginning of your day that much more pleasant.

Bonus: stretching. When you are done with the workout, stretch out slightly to loosen the muscles. Check out animals. They also stretch!

GRATITUDE

"Gratitude is not just one of the highest virtues but it's also the root of all other virtues"

Cicero

There are plenty of wonderful things happening throughout our lives: the people we love, our families working and a good concert this song, or an amazing trip. Even the simplest things can be pleasant, like the scent of grass or the feeling of the sun's rays on our skin or the sensation of the breeze upon your face. It's because the brain is naturally inclined to be focused on negative things. This is revealed in evolutionary studies in the way that humans faced various threats that included them (robbery and murder, as well as wars). To survive our brains had focus on these threats, and then respond in a pure survival needs. In order to recognize the positives is not as important as it would have to remain in the dark until the threat had been over. In the event that we miss the hungry person gazing at our food we might be taken away and then die of hunger.

What is the best time to appreciate our health? when we're sick. What is the time to appreciate the good things in life? If our life, or that of those we love are at risk.

Pause for a minute and consider this. Doesn't it seem sad to appreciate things just when we're getting ready to pass away? Are we required to be patient waiting for these occasions to appreciate the wonderful items around us? If you've guessed that answer is not true. You can develop gratitude to be a part of living. When we're happy and grateful, we don't take things as a given. We appreciate. We are grateful for what we are able to enjoy.

Imagine the seed for just a instant. What happens to seeds when we don't give it water? It dries out and dies. If we would like it to expand, or for to make it bloom then we need to water it. Then we must shine a light on the issue. If we are able to appreciate what is good then the goodness will appreciate and increases.

How can we develop gratitude? There are two ways you could do in your morning Routine:

The second is appreciating something. You could do this by enjoying a tune or eating breakfast. Choose one, and adhere to it for a short time. After that, you could choose to change your activity.

Take a cup of coffee for an example.

Be sure that there aren't any interruptions (no cellphone, no TV), ...). Breathe in, breathe out, take your time and unwind. Do you smell like coffee? Pay attention to it with all your heart and be completely present in your present. Start with a sip and enjoy it with your mouth before you swallow. Do you think it tastes good? Do you feel warm hands? You can continue this way and dedicate your full being to this experience and engaging all of your senses. In the first time you try this, you might be surprised by in the amount you like sipping your coffee.

Another way to develop gratitude is to do a simple practice. Consider and record three reasons why you're grateful. It could be something big such as a job promotion or friendship, but you can also include tiny things such as the smile you got the other day or a book you're going through. Make sure to have at least one basic item from the three.

The most important thing to do with the exercise is to contemplate each and then review the information within your mind. Spend the time not only to record it down but to concentrate, visualize the event, absorbing yourself in the moment, individual or thing. It is effective because it shifts the focus of your mind from issues that can go wrong in your life towards things you could overlook that are going very well.

As you progress, you'll start noting the wonderful moments that occur in your daily life and look forward to writing these into the journal of your Gratitude journal.

Chapter 9: Meditation

"Feelings are as if clouds move across a stormy sky. My anchor is conscious breathing."

Thich Nhat Hanh

Meditation is a huge subject. Its roots are in old religions of the East. Different meanings can be found in the context of this term, however in this article we'll be focusing on meditation that is mindful. Meditation has gained a lot of popularity across the globe in recent years thanks to research by neuroscientists. With the help of new technologies (fMRI) researchers that study the brain examined meditators for the duration of their lives (some have sat for over 500000 times!) and then scanned their brains. When they saw their brains in awe then, they thought to themselves how anyone who isn't able or unwilling to devote their whole life to meditation still gain by the method?

Enter Jon KabatZinn. Jon has played a major role by spreading the practice to the world of western culture. To prove the causation of his beliefs by conducting a research. He split subjects in two different groups. One group meditated for 45 minutes every day over eight weeks. The opposite group was a control group (they didn't practice meditation). The anxiety levels of people who practiced meditation significantly lessened during the study. Additionally, he found that they actually felt happier as well as having better moods. In only 8 weeks, He proved that through meditation, people are able to change the brain (welcome to the notion of neuroplasticity. You are welcome to explore further) to be more content, which makes their brains more open to positive feelings, and more robust in the face of difficult emotions, and perhaps even boosting their immunity.

What is the have to sit for an hour every daily? Not necessarily. Tal Ben Shahar recommends just 15 minutes per each day. Since it takes a lot of persistence endurance, patience and persistence in the beginning, many suggest beginning with only five minutes of training before gradually increasing the time when you're more confident.

How do we practice meditation?

This is an overview of the basics however, make sure you find additional sources.

Begin by sitting in a relaxed position and with an upright back. This could mean either a chair, or most commonly is a cushion placed on the flooring. Start by performing a short body scan and observing the body's sensations. Then, pay awareness to the breath. In particular, pay attention to how air moves into and exits your nostrils. Relax and breathe normally while keeping your eyes on the out and in air that is coming out of your mouth. Naturally, your mind may wander. It's normal. Simply notice the thought or feeling, maybe a pain or discomfort on your back. After that, take a moment to focus on your breathing. Repeat this practice breathing, as your anchor in your mind and your safe place to go back to.

Yoga can be a mindful substitute (or alternative) of meditation.

Additional sources:

Jon KabatZinn's book

Free guided meditation audio. This is a fantastic method to begin the practice of meditation.

I would highly suggest the "Headspace" app available on the Appstore.

JOURNALING

The keeping of a diary for personal use is an ancient ritual many have been practicing since the age of. It's nothing oldfashioned: in the course of hundreds, or perhaps thousands of years, individuals wrote down their worries as well as sorrows, disappointments desires, happiness and more. to their diary because they brought them feelings of peace, acceptance of themselves and peace of their minds. It's a simple thing but yet so effective. Research has proven the importance of writing down thoughts and experiences is beneficial to our physical and mental health.

In addition to its many benefits, journaling is proven to reduce the effects of depression, anxiety or trauma, as well as the PTSD. Also, it enhances cognitive performance and strengthens the immune system, and counteracts a lot adverse effects caused by stress, and enhances relationships.

Journaling is particularly helpful in the event of a stressful moment or experience. However, it will not only assist you in dealing with the situation and get through it, but it also will assist you in tackling similar situations. This is because it allows us to make sense of our world and understand our own and other people. Furthermore it allows us to observe and communicate our inner needs and wants.

The main rule of journaling is to remember that there aren't any regulations. You are free to write about whatever you like. The diary of your journal is a nonjudgmental and alwaysrespecting companion.

After we've discussed the practices that help us all The next thing to do is to find additional exercises you would like to incorporate into your daily routine. Look for activities you would like, are interested in, to attempt, or feel that they can benefit your health. We will provide you with various examples you could pick from. Below are some concepts to help you get inspired, all that have been tested and proven to work:

COLD SHOWER

I learned about this method by watching an Ted Talk by the famous vineloving celebrity Jerome Jarre. The process is easy, really: simply adjust the temperature of the shower until the water is coldest it will ever be. You then need to get submerged and wait for at minimum 3 minutes. It's beneficial for many reasons: first it's the ideal method to get you awake. I can assure you that you'll no longer be tired! Additionally, it releases neurochemicals which have effects of analgesia which makes us feel more sensitive to the pain. Additionally, it's been proven to boost the immune system, and alleviate signs of depression. Additionally it gives you a sensation of absolute freshness and pure after having the supplement. Not to mention the fact that you are able to face this test immediately after getting up, you are able to tackle your day with energy and vitality.

First time I had an icy shower, I started screaming as a child. It's even more difficult since you are aware of the feeling. Then, eventually, you are familiar with the. Within a couple of weeks, I was hooked to this practice. Be sure to not quit on the first day. Just be aware of the reason for doing this. Each time you shower you'll feel a sense of achievement which will motivate you further. Are you able to do what is required?

Protip 1: Start slow when you have tosimply take a normal shower then change to cold water for remaining 30 seconds. Then increase the time of exposure time slowly.

LISTEN TO MUSIC/DANCE

"Those who dance are thought to be insane by those who are unable to detect what music is going on."

George Carlin

There's really nothing that can compare to the impact of music. It is able to boost your spirits, and get you excited and prepared for the future. Though it will vary for each individual, I suggest songs which are energetic and joyful. For my playlist for the morning such as this I've included songs like "Mr Jones" by Counting Crows and "September" by Earth, Wind & Fire. It is possible to play music during your exercise routine (see below) as you shower or while making breakfast. My personal preference is to make it an intentional practice in its own (remember the exercise of gratitude that we discussed on earlier). I plug in my headphones and choose the music that is appropriate for the time and then dance in a way that no one can see and fully absorbing the tune and exuding myself. In all honesty I find it to be the time that I am most happy during my morning Routine.

There are many ways to enjoy music, but you also find other ways to appreciate music. Maybe you're a musician on the piano or guitar, or maybe you love karaoke, and sing to. Keep in mind that there's no "right method". Just follow your gut and flow with it.

Protip: look up Morning playlists on Spotify.

DECIDE AND COMPLETE YOUR 3 MIT's

"Eat live frogs early in the morning and nothing more could happen all day."

Your focus and energy levels from 8am11am, and are most wellequipped to handle difficult challenges. Make sure you are prepared for the first hour of the day like the entire life of your family depends on performing at their best. The ability to focus is the most powerful advantage in the world of constant distractions we are living in.

The book doesn't explore the intricacies of productivity and methods to control objectives and tasks within your daytoday life. But, it will explain the straightforward yet effective threeMIT method that is in the following manner:

In the evening the next day, make a list of your 3 MITS (Most Important Priorities) to do the following day. Check your calendar, ToDo list, etc. And then list just three tasks to complete the following day. The next morning, take from your todo list and shut off any distractions. Turn off notifications, switch off whatsapp, email as well as other social media. Set your smartphone to airplane mode, and go on with your work. Your 90minute work must be completed without distractions so that you can complete your 3 MIT's. It's irrelevant if you succeed in completing all three of them or only one. It is important to dedicate the time focused and determined and focus on these issues first.

Chapter 10: Breakfast

This is one of the most important. According to some, breakfast is the primary food of the day providing us with the nutrients that allows our bodies to have the necessary vitality levels required to last the day. New research has revealed that breakfast is just another food. The expert Gretchen Reynolds concluded after the study: "If you like breakfast then it's fine. If you don't, don't worry about it". But be cautious not to sacrifice your nutrition needs.

Additionally, the food you eat can be more crucial than the amount you eat. The typical glass of milk with cereals tasted great during your youth, now it's time to up the level of play. Research in nutrition has often been unpopular and are a source of confusion. Everybody claims that they have the "best" nutritional program and even scientists and experts aren't sure significantly. In this article, I'll describe a standard breakfast option that can be enjoyed by all people.

The most basic and healthy smoothie is to pick three or four fruits that are in season. Mix in a decent amount of raw oatmeal, as well as some nuts and dried fruits. Be sure to add milk or yogurt into the mixture. If you're lactose intolerant think about almond milk, or alternative options. In this case, you could mix in other ingredients that are healthy from your own choice. Blend everything together, to take your vitamins along with it.

ProTip 1: Take the entire glass of water early in the early morning. In the evening, your body loses fluids, and it's essential to replenish the fluids you drink after your first day of work.

Tip #2: If reside with a person, you should arrange for making breakfast in a way that only each person cooks all the food for your group. Set a date for a particular recipe before you agree. It can save you time.

YOURS

Consider a few minutes to think of activities that you like. It could be reading and painting or having a laugh with your companion. Maybe you'd like to create a book however you haven't had time or time to complete it. There are many of us who have children and getting their eyes with smiles on their faces is the greatest moment of your day...Everyone enjoys these things that give them pleasure as well as fun and joy. It's wonderful to set aside time time everyday to engage in things simply because you enjoy performing them without any pressures or feeling guilty. Pick at least two or three of these things now, and record them on paper. The next step is we'll be taking the activities into consideration, alongside the activities described previously in order to determine your ultimate Morning Routine.

Stop the exercise prior to continuing.

Example: Tony Robbins

Tony Robbins is the world's most renowned performance coach. He is a speaker, author and motivational speaker on the importance of success and fulfillment across all aspects of life. Tony is known as "the why Guy" and believes the idea that action with no purpose is life's drain. Tony has written a number of bestselling books (including "Awaken The Giant within") as well as coached elite celebrities like Serena Williams, Andre Agassi, Leonardo Di Caprio, Oprah and Bill Clinton. Recently, during an interview with Venture capitalist and entrepreneur Tim Ferriss, he described his Morning Routine. What would you change in your lifestyle to follow exactly the same routine Tim does in the initial period of the day? It's not a suggestion to skip everything in the book, and simply duplicate the work of Mr. Robbins (although you can). Find what's right for you, and then test the ideas of Mr. Robbins. This is the way to go:

When he wakes up, Tony immerses himself in an icy bath. After that the tub, Tony plunges into a cold tub that's 57 degrees F. The bath triggers an emotional reaction which allows for him to get up in fullon energy.

Additionally, he uses Cryotherapy A new technique that involves the use of liquid nitrogen to lower your body's temperature. It helps reduce inflammation within the body, and makes you feel feeling rejuvenated. It is, however, quite costly to purchase the equipment at your own home (local locations are beginning to pop up).

After that, he proceeds through an exercise he refers to as "Priming":

1. Inhale explosively through your nose and raise your arms. Exhale through your nostrils while pulling the arms back to the ground. Perform three sets of 30. Remember to breath rapidly and quickly.

2. In the spirit of gratitude, think of 3 factors that you're thankful for. Don't just talk about these things, but actually be aware of them and allow them to be absorbed into your heart. Include the one that's basic and tiny for example, like a cloud that is in the sky or the breeze. When we're happy we don't feel anger or not a fear.

3. Spirituality The spiritual dimension: Feel your presence with God or however you would like to identify it. Be in touch with the divine of this world. Feel at one with all things and experience how it

strengthens your relationship with others with your body, the emotions you feel, ... Experience the growth of your confidence, happiness, and drive. Next, concentrate upon your vision of living your life. Like, Tony focuses on service as it's his primary source of significance and meaning within his daily life.

4. Thirdly, concentrate on three items you'll need to create happen. Visualize them, see them as well as feel and be a part of these.

PERSONALIZE AND ORDER

Every single person has a unique fingerprint, a unique DNA. There's no one in the world who has the same traits like you. And, even more importantly than that, there'll never be anyone like you in the history of mankind. Consider the thought. Do you think it's a bit disturbing?

Our individuality is an honor and a duty. There is no one who will ever look at your way of seeing or think as you do and see the world as you do. That means that your perception of the world will be together with the way you see it. This is why I consider it our obligation to lead our lives in the way we want to lead, and also to achieve the fullest potential we can achieve. I will repeat: it's our duty to achieve our maximum potential. It is not the capacity of another person or what society claims we can achieve. Our own, unique potential!

There's no onesizefitsall answer that fits every person perfect. Only you, the reader, will know the most effective Morning Routine is. It's a responsibility and job that no one will ever remove from you. Don't worry, as this reality is positively uplifting. If you customize and personalize your routine it will be easier to transform it into something "yours" and, consequently will feel more motivated and determined to achieve success in implementing the habit in your routine and eventually getting the happiness and success you desire.

Now let's start. Now you've got an idea of around 11 things you want to integrate in your routine. Some of them were already selected from your list, which means you are already in the making. Every one of these practices in its own way will bring positive change in your lifestyle if put it into practice. Even though we strive for more change like you may are aware, carrying out every one of them will require a long time and be extremely difficult to carry out. It is necessary to choose. How many of them do we need to choose and according to what guidelines?

In the first place, ensure that you Include all of the "Positive Behaviors" described.

It's simple: research has repeatedly proven that their consistent use can bring more happiness and enjoyment. Then, review of the additional Habits along with Tony Robbins' recommendations. Which of them feel the most natural to you? Which do you think that you are in need of the most? What are the most effective ones? yield the greatest advantages? Then, what are the ones you truly desire to take on? Check them out by answering these questions, then select from 3 to 5 these behaviors based on.

Stop be sure to take this action prior to moving on.

Have you got your last personal, unofficial list of routines? Great. It's the time is finally here to purchase them. It is not often seen however it's actually crucial. Your order of how you conduct your routines will affect the efficiency of all the activities and also the mood that you are in when you start your day. In the case of exercise, it must be done before bathing and arranging your day should be done at the close of your day. Even though you'll be able to fine tune your routine in the course of time take the initiative right today to organize your routine.

From personal experience, I understand that this routine isn't easy and that's the reason I've put together an Blueprint to follow. It is not recommended to adhere to the same Morning Routine forever. Like I said, every person is unique and has each individual routine. However, you could make use of this routine to begin with, and then adapt it and alter it according to the needs and preferences of your.

MORNING ROUTINE BLUEPRINT

1. Gratitude. Sit up, smile your bedroom and reflect on two things that you are

grateful. Consider them, and then write the details down in your gratitude journal.

2. Sip a glassful of water.

3. Exercise. Do a 15minute walk, or, if willing to do it, you can try the sevenminute workout.

4. A cold shower. Do it.

5. Meditation. If you're beginning your journey five to ten minutes are enough.

6. Powerful questions. You can ask yourself a couple of questions every day.

7. Breakfast. When you are preparing breakfast, turn on some music. When eating breakfast, take a moment to slow down and pay attention (remember the practice of gratitude).

8. Finish your MIT's. Take out the 3 MIT's you picked to complete in the evening prior to bed and set aside the remaining

90 minutes to finish them in a single sitting.

So far it's been a good start. It is now time to be able to have an outline of your Morning Routine perfectly outlined and specific. It's your guide towards a better life more healthy, better and more content every day.

In this stage, it's beneficial to perform a test of your routine. Share it with your son, partner or friend as a question and inquire, not providing any explanations whether they believe they are able to perform the routine at your own pace. The purpose of this test is to see if there's sufficient accuracy in the actions required. It's crucial since you need to work efficiently and with no effort in deciding what to take the next step.

Estimate the total time required. The duration should not be more than 1 hour.

Any routine that is longer than an hour can take a long time to establish as a routine and is likely that you will fall off your track throughout the course of your journey. Make adjustments to your routine accordingly.

The only thing left to do is to take the necessary action and begin incorporating your routine to your daytoday routine. However, I'll be honest in my words: it'll not be simple. Research suggests that the 21daystoformahabitmyth may be true for very simple ones (like drinking a glass of water upon waking), but not so for more complex ones (like the one we're trying to create). In the beginning, you'll depend on your motivation to finish your routine However, once you've completed the first few days, you'll have to rely on your selfcontrol that can be a challenge, and isn't very trustworthy.

Chapter 11: Get It Done

HACK 1: IT ALL STARTS AT NIGHT

I came across this when creating my very first Morning Routine. Sometimes, I'd be able to complete the task and feel incredible: feeling energized, enthusiastic about the coming day and inspired. On other days, I'd do exactly the identical actions, and then feel tired fatigued and exhausted, then be dragging myself around. Why was this such a huge change? The difference was evident when I realized.

Based on a survey that was conducted by Gallup the majority of Americans do not get the amount recommended for sleep. It's a staggering amount. What is the price we pay to avoid sleep? A longterm lack of sleep can result in a noticeable decrease in the ability to perform and alertness. This can lead to stressinducing relationships and a poor living conditions. In addition as well, it increases chances of suffering heart attacks (and other related health problems). If you're not convinced I suggest you do some investigation. However, I'm not required to go into detail about this. It's already clear how you feel when you don't get the perfect night's sleep. Discontent, irritability, anger ,... is not the best approach to living.

The need for sleep is just like you've heard about fitness an essential human need. When we ignore the messages your body and brain is screaming to us, then we're sacrificing the life quality we want to live. Don't think of it as the loss of time. It is a way to invest in your time.

How long should you sleep? It depends. Be honest with yourself and observe. sincere (you might not agree with your answer). Be aware of how long you sleep on holidays in the absence of a schedule forcing you to sleep. The research suggests

7 to 9 hours sleep. For me as an example, my ideal length of sleep would be around 8 hours. If sleeping just 7 hours is enough to make you feel good it's okay too.

In order to help you appreciate how crucial sleep is, let me be honest with you to help you understand: If you're feeling tired all the time and drained of energy, then you're not paying enough attention because of your inability to sleep or sleep less than 7 hours per day, stop studying this book. Why? because for you, my dear sleepy dear reader, reversing this pattern is the most fundamental, and single essential action you can make to enhance your quality of daily life. I guarantee you that sleeping an extra hour can dramatically alter the way you live your life. After you've made the change then, go back to this book once more.

Protip #1: turn the screens off two hours before you go to sleep. Don't check your emails anymore or watch television or work on your laptop and connect to Facebook or text your phone. It's due to the fact that when you are exposed to a monitor, your brain believes it's daytime and your body doesn't separate Melatonin, which is which is the sleep hormone. This can be a huge change in the game. I was amazed at the speed with which I saw the changes inside me.

(Note Note: Exceptionally, when you must finish your task or other thing late at night, download f.lux on your PC. Simply search for it.).

Protip 2: for parents with children, napping can are also effective, but less than sleeping for hours. Think about a nap of 1025 minutes in the afternoon after a meal.

HACK 2: WAKE UP EARLY

The early bed time and the early rise make an individual wealthy, healthy and wise.

Benjamin Franklin

There is really just one event influencing our routine that is theoretically fixed: the time to arrive at work/school/whatever. If you were able to extend the arrival time for a mere 30 minutes, it could be a huge improvement (seriously think about speaking to your boss; you may be pleasantly shocked). Let's assume that it's repaired.

The only way we'll get the time to complete your routine is to rise early enough so that we can get into work in good time. However, at the same time we've stated that it's vital to have enough sleep. Therefore, the most important thing is to sleep in a timely manner. An example might help:

Peter must be at his work by 9am. He has to complete his routine as well as driving to work will take him two hours. He has to get up early at 7am. Additionally, Peter feels at his most at his best when he has sleeping eight hours. The ideal time for sleep for Peter is around 11pm.

How can Peter assure that he goes to sleep around 11 pm? It is important to analyze his sleeping practices. In particular, the following issues could help what you are doing in for the final two days? Does this depend solely on you or is someone else in the mix? It is the top priority to get to sleep at a reasonable time.

There is also a fact that the majority of individuals (socalled nightowls) struggle to have a tough time awakening in the early morning hours, regardless of the number of minutes of sleep they enjoy. Don't worry about it. Here are some tips:

A gradual method is to start your alarm timer 15 minutes earlier, and remain there for 2 to 4 days. On the next day, you can place it at 15 minutes earlier. Repeat.

The alarm clock should be placed away from your. Do not press snooze.

You can try the app: "Step out of Bed" to iPhone (try "Alarmy" on Android).

Keep your sleep schedule on weekends. This will let the body's natural rhythm to get you ready automatically with no alarm.

Get a refreshing shower. This is the best way to get your mind.

Remember that difficulty waking is probably due to unhealthy sleeping routines in general. This website will assist you in that.

If you believe that you are suffering from an issue with your sleeping routine and/or are having trouble getting up early at the crack of dawn, you should consider spending (at at least) an entire week get those habits in place prior to beginning with the other.

HACK 3: START SMALL, BUILD UP (optional)

It is important to keep the fact that we're certainly not trying to find a quick fix in this case. Our goal is to develop a brand different set of behaviors that pay dividends in the years ahead. It's a huge undertaking that has huge benefits. It's not worth making a decision if it's likely to be able be able to maintain it in the long term. This isn't a race It's an endurance race.

I'm sure that the initial excitement makes us be eager to begin big and put a lot of energy into the process expecting to see tangible outcomes the next day, just as we start. It's not really to blame: the modern world is constantly looking for results that are immediate and fast fixes. Each day we see advertisements and commercials promising our that if we take specific steps or purchase the product that is unique, ... then all things will be different. Is it real? Perhaps you've experienced it in your own body just like I did experienced: getting so excited about the new approach to lose weight, work out or follow the diet plan, but then when you've failed to stick with it, you'll be disappointed. Continue to try new techniques hoping that, one day through a miracle of divine intervention then you'll discover your "right solution" and adhere to the plan.

It's not how they can be formed. Two options are available for us to either continue to fool our minds or accept the that reality is as it is. developing a habit isn't an easy task. You must act the exact same manner for a few weeks before the neuronal system is set up to carry out the task effortlessly. The more complicated you create it the longer it will take to wire up the behavior, and consequently the greater chance is that you'll quit before your behavior can be changed. That's not our goal do we? !

It is not a bad idea to taking a more progressive path. The future you will be grateful to for your efforts.

"Are you suggesting I forget my Morning Routine I designed?"you may think. Not at all. The only thing I'm saying is take steps to gradually adopting the routine you've developed (and it's done by beginning with less habits).

So, review the checklist you prepared before. The goal is to streamline the morning Routine and ensure it will take no more than 30 minutes total. Here are a few examples you could follow to accomplish this:

If you choose to put off meditation until later then take three long belly breaths (abdominal breathing inflates your stomach, not your chest. You can place your hands on your stomach and observe the movement of your belly between up and down).

If you don't want to exercise instead, relax a bit and jump between the floor and up to stretch the muscles.

• Showering in the evening. If so ensure that you wash your face properly each morning in order to get your body up.

You don't have to cook breakfast. Maybe someone will take care of it, or you can find a way to reduce the time.

Set your goals for the day (decide three things to do and then look at your the calendar) during breakfast.

Consider eating a snack at home. Eat most of your breakfast at work.

It's clear that the options are limitless. When it comes to simplifying the procedure, there are a variety of things to think about to remember: First, keep in mind that you'll add different behaviors to your existing routine after you have established the simpler version. Therefore, don't fret about being unable initially to record your thoughts such as. The time will come. Keep in mind that even implementing just one from the ones we discussed about in Part 1 can bring about a positive change on your daily lifestyle. Consider your simple initial version of the plan, even if you don't apply additional behaviors to it, it'll already result in a significant positive shift for you.

HACK 4: THE 20SECOND RULE

This could be the principle that is most crucial in Part 3 and is the one that can aid you in getting things done. The principle is in Shawn Achor's novel "The Happiness Advantage".

In the beginning you should review the basic neurological functions in our brains when we try to establish an routine. According to Shawn describes in his work, brains contain millions of neurons that are interconnected through a myriad of ways to create complicated neural pathways. Along these pathways are electric currents, which ultimately form our actions and thoughts. When we do specific actions and the stronger connections are formed between neurons that are related. In turn, the more powerful this connection, the more quickly the message travels along the way. This makes it appear natural or even automatic.

Shawn is proving the fact that, as we've stated, we can't count on willpower in order to change our habits or adapt the new ways of doing things. He says: "whether it's a strict diet, a new year's resolution, or even an attempt to keep up with your guitar routine The reason that we are unable to maintain changes is that we attempt to depend on willpower." The reason? The more we utilize it, the less can use it. In our modern world, the seemingly endless number of tasks drain our strength continually.

It is the result that Shawn describes as "the the path with the least resistance". In the absence of determination, we are prone to follow the default path one that requires less effort. However, it can be detrimental to our health. This may be unconsciously and not realize that the negative effects are not insignificant. Take this as an example:

Laura has her sights set on the coming weekend with a flurry of thoughts about the possibilities she has. Would she like to mountain bike? Or visit the art museum? Her interests are numerous which she is passionate about and bring her joy It's really hard to make a decision. But, once Saturday arrives, what is she going to really do? Most likely not the thing she planned to accomplish (it's an effort!). In reality, the remote is at hand while there's a brand new TV show on...so she spends the time at the television.

As you've observed, we often follow the simplest way, that is the path with the least resistance. But, there's an option to counteract our natural instincts and to achieve the shift of behavior we wish to see.

Shawn describes the answer using a personal experience:

He set out to practice guitar each all day. He drew a graph to track his progression. But, the guitar was hidden in the closet, and was away from reach. It was not too far but the amount of time it required to go into the closet, then remove it, and then open the door to access the instrument (more than 20 minutes!) was an obstacle to the scheduled time for training. It was then a thought: "What if I could decrease the amount of activation energy I require to start?" The activation energy is the necessary energy for the beginning of a habit (in the case of this it was walking up to the closet, then opening it, and removing his guitar). Then he purchased an instrument stand and put his instrument in the central area of the bedroom. It was a good thing that after the change, he was able to practice the guitar each day.

What was Shawn accomplish that you could also do? He positioned his desired behavior on the shortest path to resistance. It made it easier for him play the guitar rather than stay away from it. Lesson learned: reduce the amount of energy that is activated by habits you wish to develop while increasing it for the habits you'd like to avoid.

Reducing the energy of activation is not only about making it simpler to accomplish. Also, it's about making our choices to make so that there is no need to consider the issue.

How can we implement this in our routine? It is essential to analyze and deconstruct the whole process carefully. Every habit you perform in your routine be aware of the trigger energy, the time and the options that you make, and the physical and mental work required to achieve it decrease the amount. If you are able to cut down the amount of energy needed to initiate those practices that contribute to achievement, just 20 seconds in time, at a time and it will not be long before you begin benefiting from their effects.

To give you an example of how you are able to take the ideas and implement into your own routine I'll make use of this Morning Routine Blueprint I explained earlier. Follow the pattern of decreasing the activation energy associated with every practice.

Gratitude:

No activation energy. Just a thought. not a need to take action or make a decision.

Take a glass of water:

The energy that activates the chakra is sent towards the kitchen and drinking a glass, then filling the glass with water. It is possible to completely eliminate this by keeping a glass close to the bed in the evening before. If you're lazy in setting the glass down on the table at night, you can keep an 8liter bottle of water within your bedroom to replenish the glass.

Exercise:

It depends on the type. Shawn For instance, he would like to run in the day, which is why he put the gym attire on and kept his running shoes close to his mattress. My situation was similar to mine. I began exercising outdoors however I realized that I required to exert too much effort. Then I changed my exercise to a 7minute exercise. My energy for activation comes from opening the application on my smartphone and it's easy.

Shower cold:

This one is tricky. The energy that is activated in this instance is psychological. In essence, it's an internal battle where one side is shouting, "don't do it! It's cold!" and the other is urging you to go for it. The choice we make is a drain on our strength. The best thing to create the rules. For instance Whatever happens you do, when I get in then count up to 10 before turning to shower. To be on the safe part, begin with warm showers, and then switch to cold showers after a few months.

Chapter 12: The 30day Morning Routine Challenge

"A journey that spans 1,000 miles starts by taking a single step"

Confucius

#morningroutinechallenge

That's the moment to be. Now is the time to end all preparatory work and begin to create a brand new method of living. We had been through a crucial process. In Part 1, we reviewed the various Positive practices derived from results from Positive Psychology. In Part 2, we discussed other practices you can incorporate into your routine and highlighted the significance of incorporating your personal habits you particularly are enjoying.

In part 3, we continued by introducing you to the most important tools are available to you to transform this idea from a dream into real. These tools can help greatly and bring about the desired outcome. They can give you that additional "push" needed to keep going.

You'll realize that by having read this far and committing to the actions you've taken in the process, you've already begun the journey towards a more satisfying and enjoyable life. This is where the real work begins. It's really motivating to draw every day on a piece of or paper (or what ever) and then keep it in view. Each day you go through your routine make sure to check your day using a light positive, positive color (I love green). It's essential to concentrate on the present moment you're currently in.

For a thorough check that we're prepared, here's an easy checklist of what you need to take care of prior to beginning the 30 Day Routine Challenge. Routine Challenge. If you need to, review the instructions in greater depth through the guide. You must go through the entire book before proceeding.

1. Pick the practices you wish to incorporate into your routine (take every aspect into consideration prior to settling).

2. You can order them

3. Check if you are able to do them all flawlessly.

4. Note the routine down as in details as you can. Anybody should be able perform the same routine without having to read at the instructions.

5. Review your sleeping habits to see if you are sleeping enough? sleep? How can you go to sleep earlier? Make these changes before you begin your challenge.

6. Reduce your routine (optional). Review the written routine and choose your most

essential routines. Discover ways to make it easier.

7. Examine each habit in detail and consider ways to cut down or even eliminate the need for energy.

8. Take action based on your research (by placing the water glass on your bed in addition).

If you've done all of the tasks listed on this list You're now ready to begin the 30 Day Routine Challenge. Routine Challenge. It doesn't matter how, you can start today: tomorrow is the best day. It's a path that can open the doors to fresh levels of health good emotions, vitality and joy. The only thing you need to do is take on a personal challenge over 30 days in consecutive row. There are no days without. If you keep it up and stick to it, you'll notice amazing improvements in yourself. It's only the beginning. After your first 30 days, you'll be able to start adding more habits into your simpler version. Within a few weeks, you'll have an hourlong routine which will totally transform your lifestyle. Be aware that the work you put into those next weeks will be rewarded throughout your existence. Most importantly take note of this: Keep moving forward, one step at an time.

Chapter 13: The Benefits Of Waking Up At 5 A.M

"Early going to sleep, then early to rise makes one well-nourished, rich and smart." Benjamin Franklin. Benjamin Franklin.

This isn't just a quaint expression, but it's a fact. There are a myriad of research studies and scientific findings showing that getting up earlier can benefit you in many ways. This includes medically emotionally, mentally, physically as well as spiritually.

All of which result in greater the success of your business and personal life.

The first person to promote the "early to be in bed early, and then up earlier to get up," wisdom was Benjamin Franklin who was one of the founder fathers and one of the signers of the Declaration of Independence for a young America. However, Franklin wasn't just the politician.

The inventor was also an writer as well as a scientist. He attributed his achievements along with numerous of his inventions due to his being the first to rise. In the years since Franklin's time, many have realized that Franklin was on the right track.

The research has proven that those who start early are more healthy, wealthy and more educated. And that's just the beginning. There are numerous benefits of waking up earlier.

If you're committed to achieving success then you must think about getting up in the early hours of five a.m. to get started on your day. Think about it this way: there are a lot more advantages beyond getting a simple two or three hours of head-start in the morning. Here are a few.

You'll be:

Restful and more relaxed. Early risers have more sleep and feel more refreshed. Why? If you sleep later and rise earlier your body is in sync to the natural cycle of circadian rhythms. Your brain adapts to the natural rhythm of day and night, both light and dark. It produces hormones, and produces the chemical the body needs to repair its own body, which results in a more relaxing sleep and a happier and healthier your.

More optimistic. The research shows that both the morning and evening crowds possess different personalities that are linked with their high-energy times. People who are night-owls are more inventive and smart, however they are also more down, gloomy and narcissistic. The morning Larks (early morning risers) are more sociable and optimistic and are generally content with their lives.

More productive. Make sure you get up a couple of hours earlier than your colleagues and witness your productivity rise. You'll not only enjoy the peace of the early morning, but you're the absence of telephone calls or screaming children (if you have children) as well as no pressures from anyone else. It's your own space and you're free to contemplate, plan and work at your own pace. Therefore, naturally, you're more productive!

A lot more family time. If you wake up early and finish your work it gives you plenty of time to spend the evenings with your loved ones. They'll be more comfortable since you don't have to worry about a list of unfinished projects. It's obvious that you'll be up early and realize you'll be able to be able to find time to get things done.

Higher grades. In 2008, a Texas University study discovered students who said they were morning people who got up earlier made higher scores. They actually scored an extra point on their GPA - earning 3.5 as opposed to 2.5 GPAs and we all are aware that higher grades can result in better employment opportunities.

Easier Commutes. If you've experienced traffic jams or struggled to get on the subway or commuter train it's likely that you've noticed an advantage of going to your work early than everyone else. morning people aren't having a problem accomplishing.

Headstart. People who get up early have an advantage on their day. They're not rushing around trying to shower, eat breakfast, make themselves ready, and take care of children or their spouses for their daily routine. They start their day calm with a sense of purpose and peace since they're awake earlier. They aren't required to rush around since they're not tardy.

More proactive. People who are early risers are more active. It's more than just a rumor. The result is the product of the research conducted by Christoph Randler, that was published in Journal of Applied Social Psychology. Randler is a professor of biology of the University of Education in Heidelberg, Germany told a reporter in The Harvard Business Review, that "...early birds tend to be more active than people who work in the evening which is why they perform very well in the business world.

They generally get higher marks in school which leads them to better schools, that then lead to better jobs."

Happier. Similar to the Randler study, studies indicate that those who wake up earlier also feel happier. The reason could be to be related to the circadian rhythm and release of chemicals and hormones that influence the way we feel within the brain. However, those who rise early are generally more content than their evening owl colleagues.

Healthier. The early risers tend to be breakfast eaters as well as exercising, both of which can lead to healthier, longer life spans.

Better Planners. Individuals who rise earlier have better plans. The peace, lack of distractions, or simply the more leisurely pace of early hour, early risers organize their work schedule, their weekends and live their lives to the fullest.

A better physical condition. The top five factors successful people perform on being up earlier in the morning is to exercise. Prior to the time their families get up and their work day begins, business professionals as well as students go to the gym, doing some running or exercising at home on apparatus.

Exercise regularly boosts their energy levels and mental state as well as gives them the vitality and concentration needed for their business. Exercise is also a great way to create longer sleep cycles that lead, naturally to more restful sleep. This is a wonderful routine to spend time with! It's also a benefit of the early morning hours and workout.

Colombia University found that people who exercise regularly have the ability to develop and sustain neurons and brain cells that reside in the hippocampus area in the brain. This particular area, known as"dentate gyrus "dentate Gyrus" is the one responsible in generating neurogenesis. Studies have also revealed that people who exercised have two to three times the growth in"the "birth rates" of neurons! Simply put, in plain English this means you're more efficient for a longer time and much less likely develop dementia when regular exercise.

Greeting the Day Instead of Dreading the Day. This is a simple idea however, when you are up earlier you can enjoy greater time to focus, less interruptions as well as the comfort of time. It's time to start your morning, enjoy the sun setting and sip a cup of coffee or tea, sit, write, stroll or just relax.

It will make you more likely to enjoy the day, rather than be anxious about it. It makes you look forward to the coming 24 hours, which means your attitude, mood and behavior are optimistic, which results in improved well-being and greater happiness.

Summary

In the past, thousands of famous or successful people have attributed their achievements in the past to having an early start to the first day of their lives. Many successful night-owls are as well, however the vast majority of successful individuals are early risers.

The many benefits overshadow any minor discomforts while you adapt to a change in time as well as routine. If you stay with the regimen, after a few some time (if it's not weeks) it will be possible to notice a positive change within your daily life, which makes it worth it.

Chapter 14: The Pros And Cons Of Rising Early

There are people who can't resist getting up around 5.30 a.m. or later. They rise in a state of blissful sleep and are eager to start the next day. We don't. The idea of waking up in the early hours of 5 a.m. requires an adjustment to. There are benefits and drawbacks to having an early start, but the main one is being unable to enjoy the benefits of a lively, yet later lifestyle. If you're someone who likes going out for dinner and sleeps in until nine or 10 p.m. could be a challenge. Therefore, you should think carefully about the choices you make.

Cons and pros of early sleepers vs. early sleepers.

There's nothing like "sleeping in" with the option of staying at home until you're ready to rising. However, the main reason that we all love lying on our beds isn't that it's so relaxing. The reason is that we're tired and don't want go out until we're refreshed. To be an early riser, you must making a commitment to an 8 p.m. sleep time and making a routine of obtaining the sleep the body requires.

It can be a relaxing experience to sleep in However, it's only for a certain amount of time. It isn't possible to "bank" sleep, like you could save calories (excess fat). There is no way to sleep for an entire week and "store in" more time for running a marathon for business the next week. The ability to recharge fully your "internal energy batteries" which allows you to use the batteries for longer. However, there is a predetermined quantity of energy, and you will get it with the correct nutrition, workout and sleep.

Advantages for being an early riser:

Rested for longer

Extra energy

Healthier

Breakfast eaters result in an increase in metabolism, which will give you the extra energy

More organised

Most likely to exercise regularly to make you healthier, slimmer and more content.

The cons of being a early riser

Don't miss out on the late evening socializing

More likely to stay up late (but will arrive later)

Can't have as many parties in the same amount, or indeed not at all

It is viewed as strange by coworkers and friends who do not have early mornings.

The advantages of being a sleeping person:

It is a good idea to work when you work in industries with late the night time times (bars or restaurants or theater)

Your boss depends on you to be all night and to work until late.

You can sleep at the same time every day.

Cons of sleeping in late:

You're less well rested.

You are less energetic

You're more likely to skip breakfast or work out

You're more likely to die earlier (one result of sleeping longer and having the effect and strain on the circadian rhythms)

Printed in the USA
CPSIA information can be obtained
at www.ICGtesting.com
CBHW071144050624
9610CB00011B/566